THE ARTS AND INDUSTRIES SERIES
William E. Warner, Consulting Editor
Frank W. Cyr, Editor of this Volume

SCIENCE EXPERIENCES
WITH
INEXPENSIVE EQUIPMENT

SCIENCE EXPERIENCES
WITH
INEXPENSIVE EQUIPMENT

by

CARLETON JOHN LYNDE, PH.D.

PROFESSOR OF PHYSICS IN
TEACHERS COLLEGE, COLUMBIA UNIVERSITY
NEW YORK CITY

INTERNATIONAL TEXTBOOK COMPANY
SCRANTON, PENNSYLVANIA
1939

INTERNATIONAL TEXTBOOK PRESS
SCRANTON, PA.

80315

Foreword

It is evident from the sales of Science Experiences with Home Equipment that a great many of you find fun in making things happen with simple equipment and satisfaction in knowing why they happen.

This second book, Science Experiences with Inexpensive Equipment, leads you farther along the same way. It illustrates, describes and explains two hundred new science experiences. For the first eighty-four of these experiences, you require only home equipment, and for the remaining one hundred and sixteen you need in addition the inexpensive equipment described on pages 209 to 222.

Most of these new science experiences are more difficult than those in the first book. But each step of each experience is carefully illustrated and described and if you follow these directions accurately you will succeed in every case.

The writer hopes and believes that you will have as much fun and satisfaction with these experiences as you had with those described in the first book.

"Knowledge begins in wonder."

"All thought is based on experience."

"One experience is worth ten demonstrations."

Acknowledgment

The writer wishes to thank his colleagues, Professors Maurice A. Bigelow, Samuel Ralph Powers, Gerald S. Craig and Frank W. Cyr, for steady encouragement in the preparation of this series of books; and Professor Parke B. Fraim, Polytechnic Institute of Brooklyn, for excellent experiences.

He wishes to thank also the following members of his classes for suggestions included in the series: Lincoln Baar, Clarence E. Baer, Frederick W. Bates, Mark P. Bedford, Joseph M. Cadbury, Eleanor Cleveland, Thomas F. Dolan, Neil C. Doren, James K. Harris, Edgar M. Hoopes, John Dale Kelly, James F. Mason, Jesse V. Miller, Paul C. Mitchell, Ralph Preston, Charles E. Reck, Allan Scholtzhauer, C. Neale Stacy, Rudolph Steinberg, Karl Theman, Loring E. Tyson, Etta Ward Hastings, Robert S. Wheelock, Lester R. Willard, and Edith Yelenfy.

TABLE OF CONTENTS

BASEBALL CURVES AND THE LIKE

CENTRIFUGAL FORCE

OTHER MECHANICAL PRINCIPLES

G<small>ASES</small>

L<small>IQUIDS</small>

H<small>EAT</small>

WATER PRESSURE

ATMOSPHERIC PRESSURE

SIPHONS

AIR COMPRESSED AND EXPANDED

OTHER GASES

SCIENCE EXPERIENCES
WITH
INEXPENSIVE EQUIPMENT

Baseball Curves and the Like

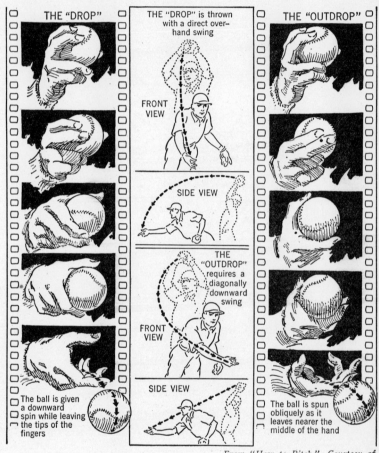

THE "DROP"

THE "DROP" is thrown with a direct overhand swing

FRONT VIEW

SIDE VIEW

THE "OUTDROP" requires a diagonally downward swing

FRONT VIEW

SIDE VIEW

THE "OUTDROP"

The ball is given a downward spin while leaving the tips of the fingers

The ball is spun obliquely as it leaves nearer the middle of the hand

From "How to Pitch." Courtesy of A. G. Spalding and Bros., New York.

1. How to Curve a Baseball

The ball "follows its front." That is, it curves in the direction in which its front is turning.

Why?   See page 223

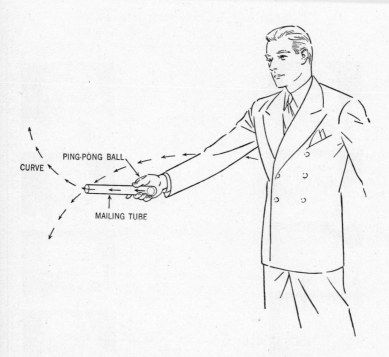

CURVE

PING-PONG BALL

MAILING TUBE

2. To Throw Curves with a Ping-pong Ball

Find or make a cylindrical cardboard mailing tube about 1 foot long and with an inside diameter about ½ inch larger than the outside diameter of the ping-pong ball.

Go outside where you will have plenty of room, place the ball in the tube, and swing the tube to throw the ball.

You will throw beautiful curves but you will not have much control.

The ball will always curve in a direction opposite to that in which you swing the tube. If you swing the tube from right to left, the ball will curve from left to right, and vice versa.

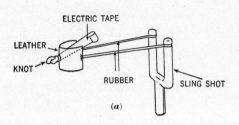

(a)

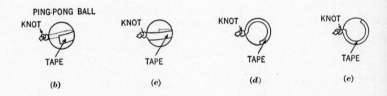

(b)   (c)   (d)   (e)

3. Another Way to Throw Curves

a. Use a sling-shot with arms about 4 inches high and 5
inches apart. Make a small hole in the leather, insert
a 6-inch length of electric tape and tie a knot.

b. Wrap the tape around the ping-pong ball as shown here
and shoot the ball as you would a stone.
It will curve *out* to the left.

c. Repeat with the tape as shown. The ball will curve *in*
to the right.

d. Repeat with the tape as shown. The ball will curve
up.

e. Repeat with the tape as shown. The ball will curve
down.

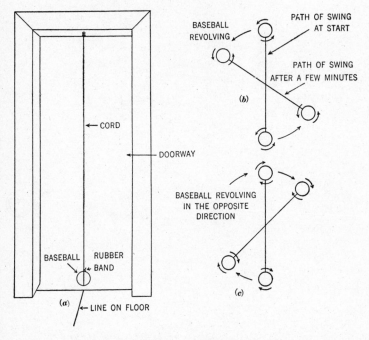

4. To Show the Sidewise Shift of a Revolving Baseball

a. Hang a baseball about 2 inches above the floor in a doorway and twirl it until the cord has been shortened about 4 inches by the twisting. Swing the baseball as a pendulum above a line drawn on the floor and it will revolve rapidly as the cord untwists.

b. If the baseball revolves as shown here, it will *follow its front* on each forward swing and move slightly to the *left*. It will also *follow its front* on each backward swing and move slightly to the *right*.

As a result, its path of swing will shift as shown.

c. If the ball revolves in the *opposite direction*, its path of swing will shift in the *opposite* direction.

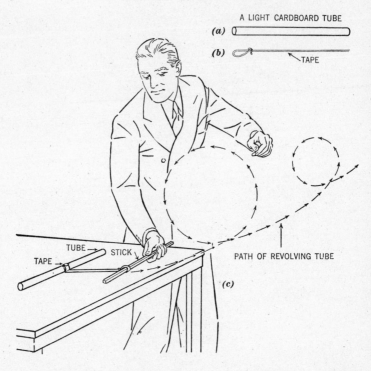

A LIGHT CARDBOARD TUBE
(a)
(b) TAPE
TUBE STICK
TAPE
PATH OF REVOLVING TUBE
(c)

5. To Make a Tube Curve Through 360° or More

a. Find a *very light* cardboard tube about 1 inch in diameter and 1 foot to 2 feet long. The *light* cardboard tubes, which come around long candles sold in the ten-cent stores, are excellent. *The tube must be light in weight.*

b. Buy a yard of cotton tape ½ inch to ¾ inch wide and make a 3 inch loop at one end.

c. Wind the tape around the tube *at the exact middle* in such direction that when it unwinds it will make the tube revolve with its front moving *upward.*

Place the tube on a table, insert a 3-foot stick in the loop and flick the tape rapidly.

The tube will curve in the air in one complete loop and sometimes in two, as shown.

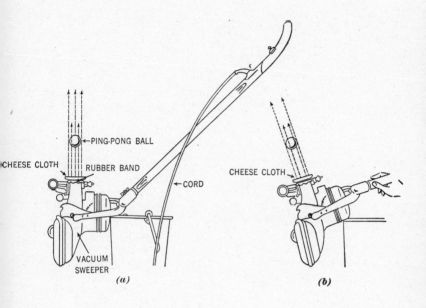

Labels within figure: PING-PONG BALL, CHEESE CLOTH, RUBBER BAND, CORD, VACUUM SWEEPER, (a), CHEESE CLOTH, (b)

6. The Air Stream Supports and Holds the Ball

a. Remove the bag from a vacuum sweeper. Support the sweeper on a table in such position that the outlet points vertically upward. Fasten a 6" x 6" piece of cheesecloth over the outlet by means of a doubled rubber band. Start the motor at top speed and put a ping-pong ball in the vertical air stream about 6 inches above the outlet.

The air stream will keep the ball bobbing up and down.

b. Tilt the sweeper very slowly and the ball will remain bobbing in the air stream until the angle is about 10° or 15° from the vertical.

Note. The cheesecloth makes the air stream fairly uniform. It should have very open mesh to let the air through freely.

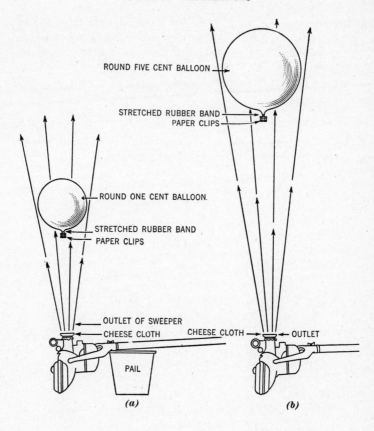

ROUND FIVE CENT BALLOON

STRETCHED RUBBER BAND
PAPER CLIPS

ROUND ONE CENT BALLOON.

STRETCHED RUBBER BAND
PAPER CLIPS

OUTLET OF SWEEPER
CHEESE CLOTH   CHEESE CLOTH   OUTLET

PAIL

(a)   *(b)*

7. The Air Stream Supports and Holds the Balloons

a. Blow up a *round* one-cent balloon until it has a volume of about
one quart and tie it. Place it in the air stream of the vacuum
sweeper and attach paper clips as weights until it floats about
2 or 3 feet above the outlet.

The air stream will cling to the balloon and keep it bobbing up
and down.

Tilt the sweeper slowly.

The balloon will remain bobbing in the air stream until the
angle is 10° or 15° from the vertical.

b. Blow up a round five-cent balloon until it is very large and tie it. Place it in the air stream and add paper clips as weights, if necessary, to keep it floating about 6 or 8 feet above the outlet.

The air stream will cling to the balloon and keep it bobbing up and down.

Tilt the sweeper slowly.

The balloon will continue to bob up and down in the air stream until the angle is 10° to 15° from the vertical.

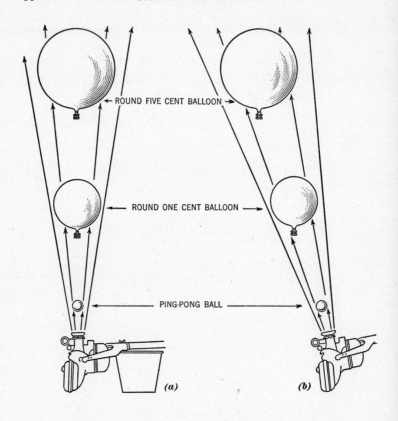

← ROUND FIVE CENT BALLOON →

← ROUND ONE CENT BALLOON →

← PING-PONG BALL →

(a) *(b)*

8. The Air Stream Supports and Holds the Ball and Balloons

a. Put the ping-pong ball, small balloon, and large balloon one after another into the vertical air stream.

They will bob up and down one above another.

b. Tilt the air stream very slowly.

They will remain bobbing in the stream until the angle is 10° to 15° from the vertical.

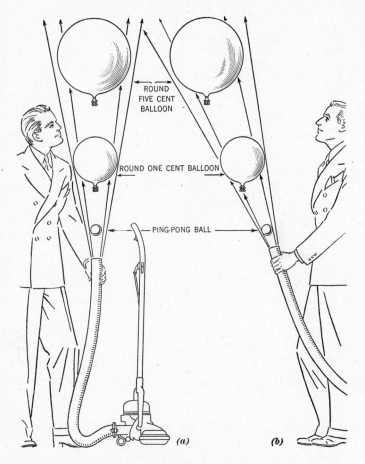

9. The Air Stream Takes the Ball and Balloons for a Walk

a. Remove the cheesecloth from the outlet of the vacuum sweeper and attach the hose without cheesecloth or nozzle.

Start the motor and let one experimenter hold the end of the hose pointing vertically upward while another puts into the air stream the ping-pong ball, small balloon, and large balloon, one after another.

They will bob up and down together one above another.

Let the first experimenter walk around slowly while keeping the air stream vertical.

The ball and balloons will remain in the air stream.

b. Let the first experimenter tilt the air stream slowly.

The ball and balloons will remain in the air stream until the angle is about 10° to 15°.

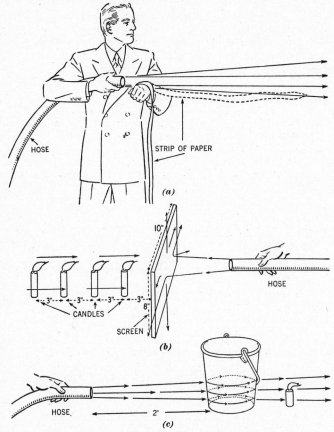

10. Other Air-Stream Experiences

a. The air stream lifts the paper.

Hang a strip of newspaper about 3′ x 4″ over one hand and shoot the air stream over its upper end.

The air stream will lift the paper.

b. The air stream blows the flames toward the screen.

Make the test illustrated and notice that the flames bend *toward* the screen.

c. The air stream appears to go through a pail.

Start the test as shown and move the hose slowly toward the pail. The air stream will blow out the candle.

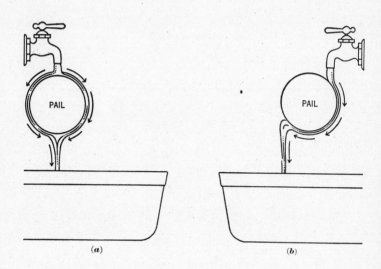

(a)   (b)

11. The Water Stream Clings to Objects

a. Let the stream from a water faucet strike the top of the curved side of a pail.

    The stream will divide and spread out, but the two halves will cling to the sides of the pail and meet below.

b. Let the water stream strike the side of the curve.

    The stream will spread out but it will cling to the pail and leave it nearly opposite the point at which it strikes.

c. Repeat *a* and *b* with a *smooth* tumbler.

    You will get similar results.

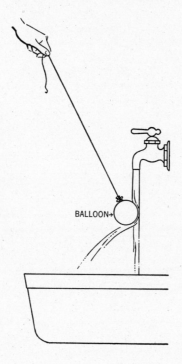

12. The Water Stream Clings to the Balloon

Blow up a balloon and tie it with a cord about 3 feet long. Swing the balloon as a pendulum and let it strike the water stream from a faucet.

The water stream will hold the balloon and part of it will curve under the balloon.

You will feel the pull of the water.

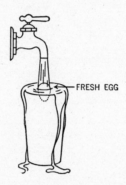

FRESH EGG

13. The Water Stream Lifts the Egg

Place a fresh egg in a tumbler of water and it will sink to the bottom.

Place the tumbler and egg under a water faucet and gradually turn on the water more and more.

When the water stream has more than a certain velocity it will lift the egg up against the force of the stream and apparently try to lift it out of the tumbler.

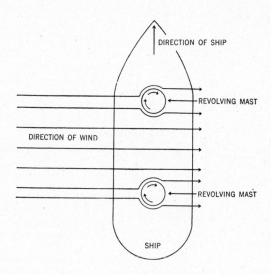

14. A Ship with Revolving Masts

Some years ago a German named Flettner constructed a ship with revolving masts and sailed it to America and back by wind power.

Each mast was a tall hollow metal cylinder of large diameter revolved at high speed by a motor.

If the directions of the wind and of the revolutions were as above, the atmosphere would force each mast to *follow its front,* or windward side, and move the ship forward.

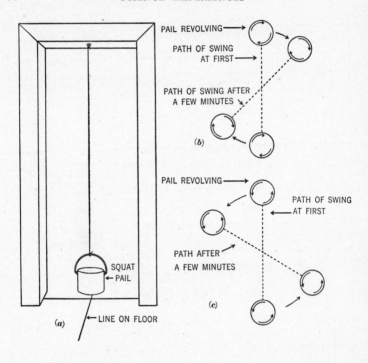

15. To Illustrate the Action of a Revolving Mast

a. Suspend an empty pail in a doorway on a cord long enough to bring it within 2 inches of the door sill. Turn the pail to twist the cord and continue until the cord has been shortened 4 inches or more by twisting. Swing the pail as a pendulum.

b. If the pail revolves as shown here, it will *follow its front* on each forward swing and move slightly to the *right*. It will also *follow its front* on each back swing and move slightly to the *left;* as a result its path of swing will shift more and more, as shown.

c. If the pail revolves in the opposite direction, its path of swing will shift in the opposite direction, because the pail *follows its front.*

Use a pail broader than it is deep. It will not wobble. See Experience 19.

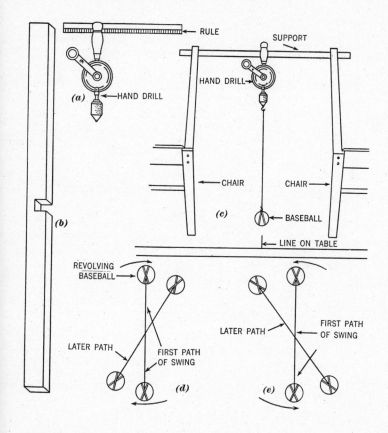

16. Another Demonstration of the Sidewise Shift of a Revolving Baseball

a. Find a hand drill and measure the width of its handle.

b. Find a soft wood board about 4′ x 2½″ x 1″ and at its middle cut a slot about $\frac{1}{16}$ inch narrower than the width of the drill handle.

c. Drive the handle into the slot and support the hand drill between two chairs on a table. Fasten in the chuck a small screw-eye (18 for 5 cents). Attach

one end of a *light* cord to the eye and the other end
to a rubber band stretched around a baseball. Make
the length of the cord such that the ball is about 2
inches above the table. Draw a line on the table,
swing the baseball as a pendulum above this line,
and turn the drill.

d. The baseball will "follow its front" as in Experience 4.
Turn the drill handle clockwise and the path will shift
in the direction shown.

e. Turn the handle counter-clockwise and the path will
shift in the opposite direction.

Centrifugal Force

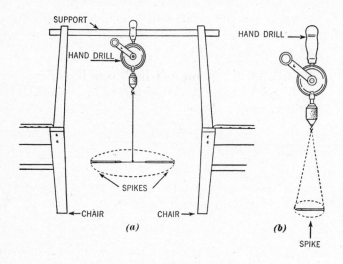

(a)   *(b)*

17. Centrifugal Force with Spikes

a. Fasten the point of each of two similar spikes to a 6-inch cord. Tie one end of a *light* string to the middle of the 6-inch cord and the other end to a screw-eye. Make the length of the string such that the heads of the spikes will be about 2 inches above the table when the screw-eye is in the chuck of the hand drill. Fasten the screw-eye in the chuck and turn the drill.

The spikes will rise until they revolve in a horizontal plane.

b. Suspend a single spike from a light string and screw-eye.
Fasten the screw-eye in the chuck and turn the drill.

The spike will rise and revolve in a horizontal plane.

Why? See page 225

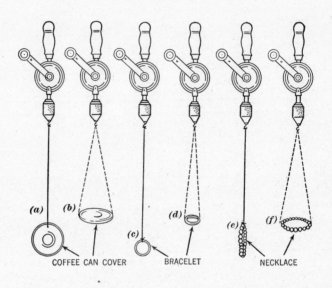

COFFEE CAN COVER   BRACELET   NECKLACE

18. Centrifugal Force with a Coffee Can Cover, Bracelet, and Necklace

a. Punch a nail hole near the edge of a coffee can cover and support the cover as shown.

b. Turn the drill and you will see the cover rise and revolve in a horizontal plane.

c. Support a bracelet as shown.

d. Turn the drill and you will see the bracelet rise and revolve in a horizontal plane.

e. Support a *short, light* necklace or chain, as shown.

f. Turn the handle and you will see the necklace rise and revolve in a horizontal plane.

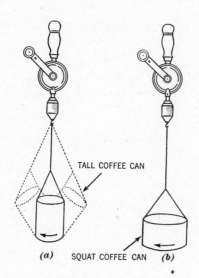

TALL COFFEE CAN

(a)   SQUAT COFFEE CAN   *(b)*

19. Centrifugal Force with Coffee Cans

a. Find a *tall,* one-pound coffee can, punch a nail hole near the open end and punch another hole exactly opposite the first. Tie a short string in the holes for a handle, attach one end of a *light* string to the middle of the handle and a screw-eye to the other.

Fasten the screw-eye in the chuck and turn the drill.

The can will revolve but it will *wobble badly* as though it were trying to revolve on its side.

b. Find a *squat,* one-pound coffee can and repeat *a.* The can will revolve but it *will not wobble.*

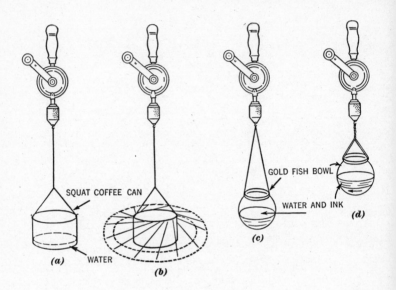

20. Centrifugal Force with Water

a. Repeat *b*, Experience 19, but before you start pour water into the can to a depth of one-half inch.

b. Turn the handle and you will see the water crawl up inside the can and over the top.   It will scatter in a circle on the table.

c. Support a small, *squat, spherical* goldfish bowl or flower bowl as shown. Pour water into it to a depth of one inch and add a half-teaspoonful of ink to color it.

d. Turn the handle and you will see the water leave the bottom of the bowl.   It will form a circular band at the middle.

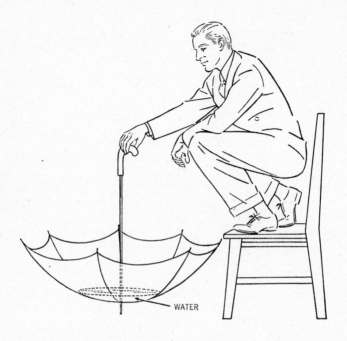

WATER

21. Centrifugal Force with an Umbrella

Open an umbrella, pour a tumbler of water into it, stand on a chair, and twirl the umbrella.

You will see the water fly out over the edge and make a circle on the floor.

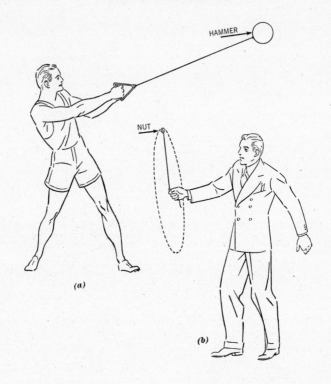

22. To Feel Centrifugal Force

a. Centrifugal force and the hammer throw.

Turn two or three times rapidly to give the hammer high speed.

The centrifugal force on your hands and arms will be very great.

b. Centrifugal force with a light weight.

Tie an iron nut or other light weight to the end of a *stout* cord and whirl it in a circle.

The greater the weight and the faster it moves, the greater will be the centrifugal force with which it pulls away from your hand.

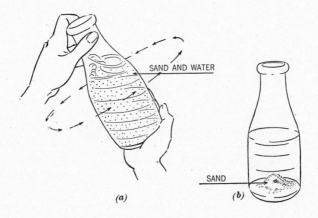

SAND AND WATER

SAND

(a) *(b)*

23. Is This Centrifugal Force?

a. Put a handful of sand or earth into a quart milk bottle, fill the bottle half full of water, put on the cap and shake the bottle in a circle to set the water turning in a circle.

b. Stand the bottle on the table and let the water come to rest. You will find the sand or earth at the *center* of the bottom instead of at the edge.

Other Mechanical Principles

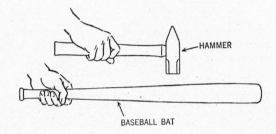

24. To Find the "Best Spot" on a Bat

Hold the bat in one hand and strike it with a hammer at each inch along its length.

You will find one spot where the bat *does not* sting your hand. This is the best spot at which to hit the ball with the bat. Mark it with a circle around the bat.

Why? See page 226.

From "How to Pitch." Courtesy of
A. G. Spalding and Bros., New York.

25. To Pitch a Fast Ball

Swing your hand, arm, and body rapidly in the largest
possible circle to give the ball at the circumference
the greatest possible speed.

26. How Fast Can You Throw a Baseball?

Throw the ball vertically upward, while a friend takes the time in seconds from the instant the ball leaves your hand until it strikes the ground.

Half this time multiplied by 32 is the velocity in feet per second you gave the ball.

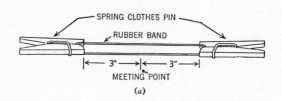

SPRING CLOTHES PIN

RUBBER BAND

|← 3" →|← 3" →|

MEETING POINT

(a)

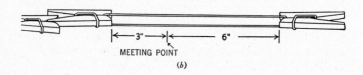

|← 3" →|← 6" →|

MEETING POINT

(b)

27. The Lighter the Faster

a. Stretch a light rubber band to 6 inches between two spring clothes-pins on a smooth table and release the pins at the same instant.

The pins will meet at the middle point.

b. Clamp two clothes-pins together to double the weight at one end. Stretch the rubber band to 9 inches and release the pins at the same instant.

The pins will meet 6 inches from the single pin and 3 inches from the two pins.

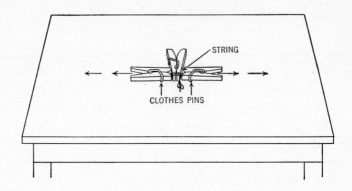

28. Force and Motion

a. Tie the handles of a spring clothes-pin together with *one* loop of string.

Place this clothes-pin at the middle of a smooth table and place two other clothes-pins beside it, one against the end of each handle.

Burn the string, and the handles, in springing apart, will give the side clothes-pins equal speeds in opposite directions.

b. Repeat the experience with two clothes-pins clamped together on one side and one on the other.
The two will acquire half the speed of the single pin.

c. Tie the handles together as in *a,* place one handle against a heavy book, and place a single clothes-pin against the other handle.

Burn the string and the single clothes-pin will be given twice the speed of a single pin in *a.*

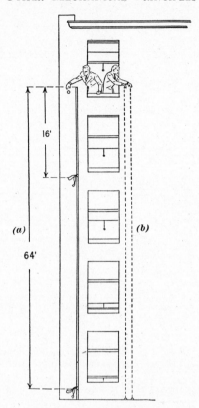

16'

(a)   (b)

64'

29. Falling Bodies

a. The farther the faster.

Find a long string and tie a colored ribbon 16 feet from one end and another 64 feet from the same end.

Hang this string out of a window in a tall building and time the fall of stones.

You will find that each stone falls 16 feet in the first second and 64 feet in the first two seconds.

That is, the farther it falls the faster it goes.

b. Galileo's experience.

Drop a large stone and a small stone at the same instant from the same height. They will fall side by side.

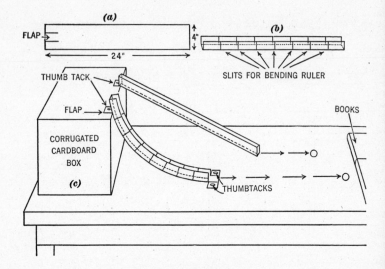

30. The Curved Ski Chute is the Faster

a. Cut two strips of heavy wrapping paper 24″ x 4″ and cut a
1″ x 1″ flap at the middle of one end of each.

b. Bend up the sides 1½ inches on each to make chutes. In one
chute cut slits in the sides at 3-inch intervals for ease in
bending.

c. Fasten the flap of each to a corrugated cardboard box by means
of a thumb tack.

Bend the chute with slits and fasten its lower end to the table
with thumb tacks as shown.

Place a row of books 2 or 3 feet from the ends of the chutes and
release at the same instant a marble at the top of each chute.

The marble in the curved chute will reach the books first.

Exchange the marbles and repeat.

d. Pull the box back to straighten the curved chute.

The marbles will now reach the books at the same instant.

Note. On the curved chute have the lower part of each slit on the
outside of the chute where it cannot delay the marble.

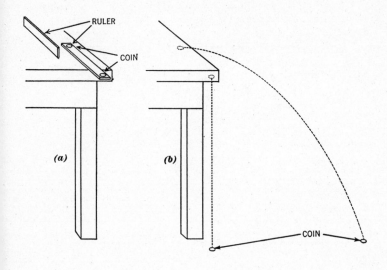

31. They Reach the Ground in the Same Time

a. Place two coins on a ruler; one at one end on the table and the other at the other end which projects over the edge of the table.

b. Hit the end on the table a horizontal blow with a second ruler. The coins will land at the same instant although one travels farther than the other.

(a)

(b)

(c)

32. The Broad Jump

The next time you practice the broad jump try this:

a. Run fast.

b. Jump *upward* from the take-off.

c. The run gives you horizontal speed, the upward jump gives you time in the air. The combination gives you a long jump.

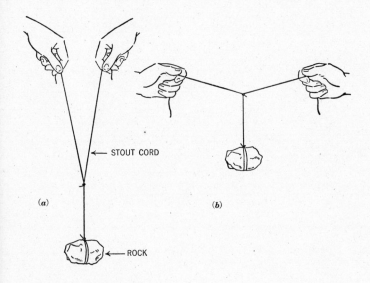

— STOUT CORD

(a)   (b)

— ROCK

33. You Cannot Straighten the Cord

a. Find a rock weighing about 2 lbs. and support it from the middle of a stout cord.

b. Try to pull hard enough to straighten the cord. You will find that you cannot do so.

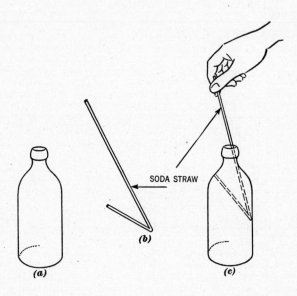

SODA STRAW

(a)   *(b)*   *(c)*

34. To Lift a Bottle with a Soda Straw

a. Find a bottle with a *short* neck.

b. Bend a soda straw about ⅓ way from one end.

c. Insert the bent end into the bottle and lift the straw. You will lift the bottle easily.

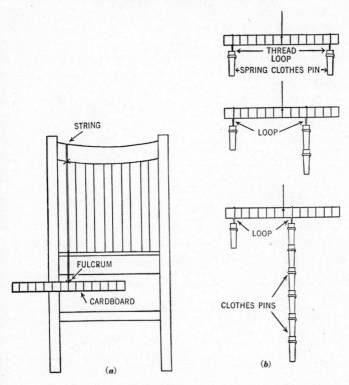

35. Balance

a. Cut out a piece of cardboard 13″ x 1″ and attach a supporting cord at the exact middle and near the top.   Mark off six 1-inch spaces on each side of this middle point or fulcrum. Hang this balance from the back of a chair or other support and make it balance exactly by cutting off a little from the heavier side.

b. Tie pieces of thread 6 inches long into loops about 2½ inches long to support the weights.

Use spring clothes-pins as weights and you can balance them in many ways.

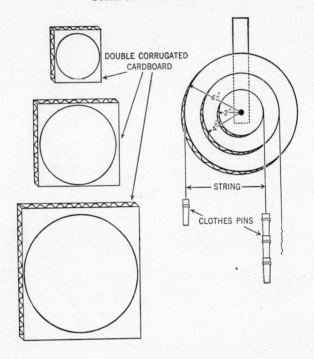

36. Pulleys

Draw circles of 6-inch radius about the same center but on opposite sides of double corrugated cardboard, cut out the pulley and make a shallow groove in its rim by pressing in gently with the back of a knife blade.

Repeat with pulleys of 4-inch and 2-inch radius.

Glue the pulleys together and mount them so that they turn easily on a common axle—a nail.

Wind a thread in the groove of each pulley and attach it at one end.

One clothes-pin will balance three or two will balance three, according to the arrangement.

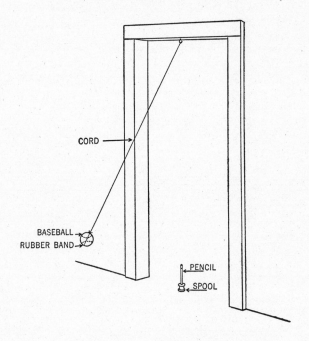

37. Pendulum Game

Tie one end of a cord to a rubber band and stretch the band around a baseball.

Suspend this pendulum in a doorway and make its length such that the ball hits the top half of a pencil which stands in the hole of a spool on the door sill.

Place the pencil and spool in such position that the top of the pencil is hit when the ball is at the lowest part of a straight forward swing.

Now draw the ball back about 4 feet and try to swing it in such a way that it *misses* the pencil on the *forward swing* and *strikes* it on the *back swing*.

It is difficult to do.

Use only *one* to-and-fro swing at each trial.

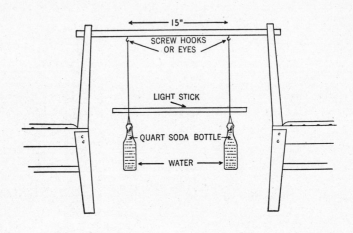

38. Alternating Pendulums

Arrange the equipment, with two pendulums of exactly the same length.

Hold one bottle and start the other swinging as a pendulum, then release the first bottle.

The swinging pendulum will gradually stop and the second pendulum will gradually start swinging.

Then the second pendulum will slowly stop and the first will start swinging again, and so on.

Gases

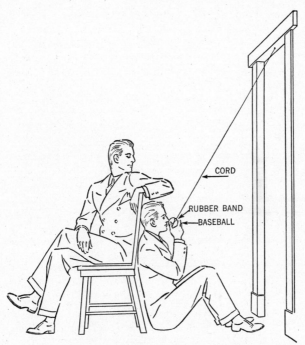

CORD

RUBBER BAND
BASEBALL

39. Nose Pendulum

Make up a baseball pendulum. Sit on the floor with the
back of your head against the back of a chair on which
someone is sitting.

Hold the baseball against your nose and release it.

You will think it is going to hit your nose on the return
swing, but it will not, unless you give it a push at the
start.

Why?   See page 230

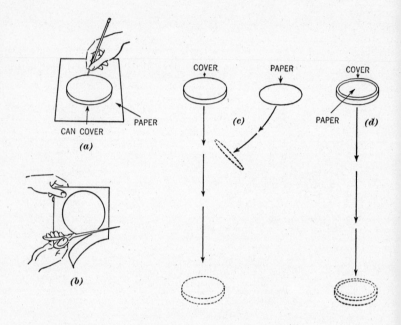

40. Air Resistance

a. Place a coffee-can cover on a piece of paper and draw a circle the size of the cover.

b. Cut out a circle of paper *a little smaller* than the can cover.

c. Hold the cover and paper horizontally side by side and drop them.

   The cover will reach the floor first.

d. Place the paper on the cover and drop them.
   They will reach the floor together.

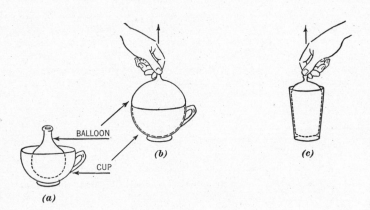

(a)

(b)

(c)

BALLOON

CUP

41. To Lift a Teacup or Tumbler with a Balloon

a. Hold a balloon inside a tea cup with its lower end near or touching the bottom of the cup.

b. Blow up the balloon, close it, and lift it by its neck. The balloon will support the cup.

c. Repeat *a* and *b* with a tumbler.

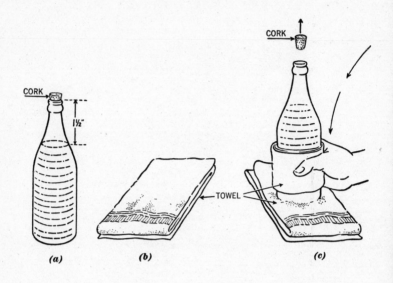

42. To Remove a Cork without Touching It

a. Fill a pint soda bottle with water *to within one and one-half inches of the top* and close it with a *cork* stopper.

b. Fold a thick bath towel for a cushion and place it on the floor or other solid support.

c. Wrap the bottle in another towel to protect your hand from broken glass, if any. Bring the bottle down with considerable force on the cushion and the cork will fly out after a few blows.

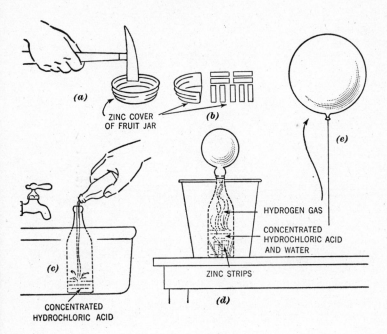

ZINC COVER
OF FRUIT JAR

(a)

(b)

(e)

HYDROGEN GAS

CONCENTRATED
HYDROCHLORIC ACID
AND WATER

(c)

ZINC STRIPS

(d)

CONCENTRATED
HYDROCHLORIC ACID

43. To Fill a Balloon with Hydrogen

a. Buy a five-cent zinc fruit-jar cover and break away the glass lining.

b. Cut the zinc cover in half and cut one-half into strips which will go into the mouth of a pint soda bottle.

c. Buy two ounces of concentrated hydrochloric acid at a drug store and handle it with the greatest care, so that it will not burn you or your clothes.

Stand a pint soda bottle in a sink, pour into it the two ounces of concentrated hydrochloric acid, then run two ounces of water into the acid bottle and pour it into the soda bottle.

d. Stand the soda bottle in a sink or pail for safety, drop *all* of the zinc strips into the acid, and pull the wet mouth of a small one-cent balloon over the wet mouth of the bottle.

The balloon will rise.

e. After the zinc and acid have stopped producing hydrogen, tie the balloon and release it.

The balloon will float.

Warning. Do not get acid on yourself or your clothes. It will burn very badly. When you have finished rinse the bottles inside and out with plenty of water.

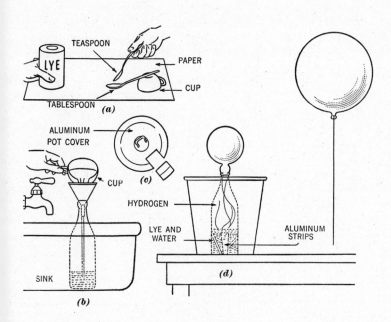

44. Another Way to Fill a Balloon with Hydrogen

a. Put down a piece of paper and stand on it a can of household lye and a tablespoon with its handle on an inverted cup.

Use a teaspoon to fill the tablespoon *level full* of lye.

Put the cover on the lye can at once or the lye will take water from the air.

b. Put the lye into the cup and add exactly six tablespoonfuls of water. Stand a pint soda bottle in a sink and pour the dissolved lye into the bottle. Rinse the cup and spoons, fold the paper and throw it away.

c. Cut exactly a 2″ x 2″ piece from a ten-cent *aluminum* pot cover or baking pan. Cut it into strips small enough to go into the bottle.

d. Stand the bottle in a pail or sink for safety, drop *all* the aluminum strips into the lye and pull the wet mouth of a small one-cent balloon over the wet mouth of the bottle.

In 30 minutes the balloon will be filled with hydrogen. Tie it and detach it.

It will rise.

Rinse out the bottle with plenty of water.

Warning. Do not get lye on your hands or clothes. It will burn very badly.

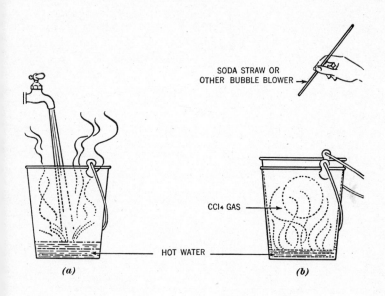

SODA STRAW OR
OTHER BUBBLE BLOWER →

CCl₄ GAS →

HOT WATER

(a)   (b)

45. Carbon-Tetrachloride Gas

a. Pour about two quarts of *hot* water into an empty 12-quart pail.

b. Stand another empty 12-quart pail in the hot water to heat it and pour a half cup of carbon-tetrachloride liquid into the warm pail; wait about five minutes for the warmed liquid to form a gas; then blow a large soap bubble and drop it into the pail.

The soap bubble will float in the carbon-tetrachloride gas.

Carbon-tetrachloride (C Cl_4) is a cleaning fluid which does not burn. It can be bought at a drug store for forty cents a can.

If you have only one large pail, turn it upside down in a sink and pour very hot water over it to warm it. Then turn it right side up and pour in the carbon-tetrachloride liquid.

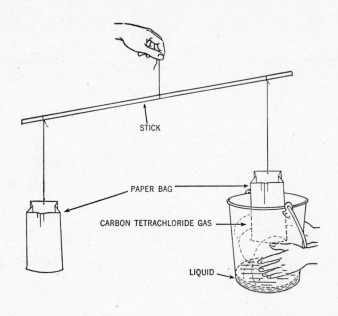

STICK

PAPER BAG

CARBON TETRACHLORIDE GAS

LIQUID

46. Another Demonstration of Gas Buoyancy

Balance a yardstick or other stick with one broad side on
top. Hang on it two paper bags of the same size and
balance them.

Let one experimenter hold the paper bag balance while
another *lifts* the pail up under one bag.

The carbon-tetrachloride gas will lift the bag.

Note. Do not let the bag touch the liquid.

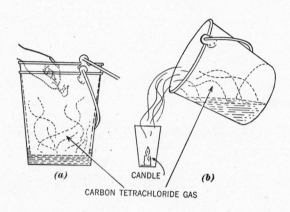

(a)   CANDLE   (b)

CARBON TETRACHLORIDE GAS

47. The Gas Puts Out Fire and Pours

a. Light a match and move it down slowly into the carbon-tetrachloride gas.

The gas will put out the fire.

b. Place a *short* piece of candle in a tumbler and light it, then tilt the pail over the tumbler to let the gas pour, but not the liquid.

The gas will pour as though it were a liquid, and extinguish the candle.

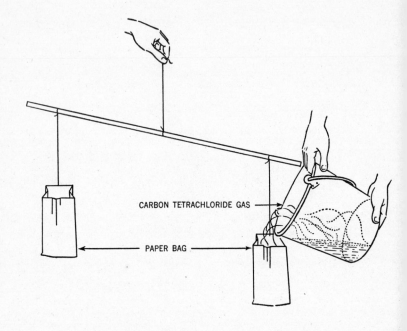

CARBON TETRACHLORIDE GAS →

←——— PAPER BAG ———→

48. The Gas is Heavier than Air

Let one experimenter hold the paper bag balance and one
    bag, while another fills the other bag with carbon-
    tetrachloride gas.

The filled bag will sink when released.

Pour the liquid carbon-tetrachloride back into its can,
    to save it.

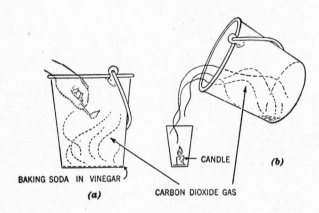

49. Carbon-Dioxide Gas

a. Pour a half tumbler of vinegar into a 12-quart pail and
add two level tablespoonfuls of baking soda.

They will fizz and produce carbon-dioxide gas.

Lower a lighted match into the gas and it will go out.

b. Tilt the pail over a tumbler containing a *short* lighted
candle.

The gas will pour and extinguish the candle.

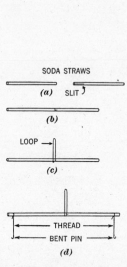

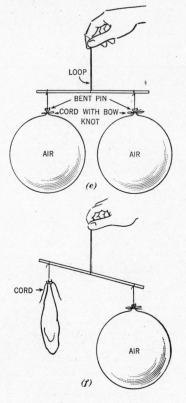

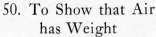

50. To Show that Air has Weight

a. Select two soda straws and slit one end of one for a distance of 1 inch.

b. Shove the slit end into one end of the second straw.

c. Support the straws on a loop of twine and balance them.

d. Cut two threads 8 inches long and tie a bent pin near one end of each. Tie one thread near each end of the straws and balance them.

e. Blow up two large round five-cent balloons.

Tie each with thick cotton *cord* and a bow knot.

Shove a bent pin point through the mouth rim of each and balance the balloons by shifting the loop.

f. Hold one balloon, untie the cotton cord on the other to let out the air, and hang the cotton cord over the pin.

The balloon filled with air will sink when released and lift the empty balloon.

Liquids

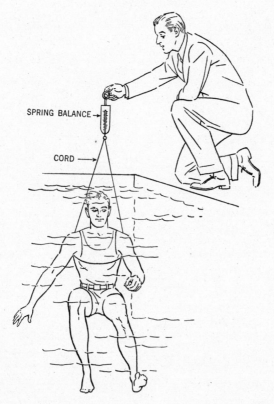

SPRING BALANCE →

CORD →

51. You Weigh Very Little in Water

At the swimming pool, tie an 8-foot cord into a 4-foot loop, pass it across your chest and under your arms and have a friend weigh you *when you have exhaled and are entirely submerged.* You will weigh very little.

Weigh a number of friends in this way.

You will find that some have no weight at all—the floaters. Others will weigh from one to five pounds.

Why? See page 232

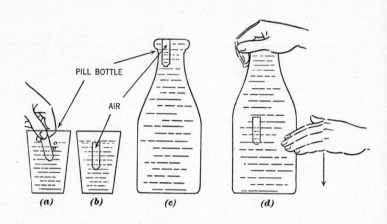

52. An Obedient Diver

a. Find a very small glass pill bottle. Place it mouth
down in a tumbler of water and tilt it to let air escape. Let the bottle float.

b. Continue to let air escape until you see the closed end
of the *floating* bottle just *under* the surface, when
you look at the under side of the surface of the water
through the side of the tumbler.

c. Put a finger over the mouth of the bottle, transfer the
bottle to a quart milk bottle *full to the top* with
water, and remove your finger *under water*.

d. Place the palm of your *right* hand over the mouth of
the full bottle. Make a downward motion with your
left hand and press down with your right.

The small bottle will dive.

Make an upward motion with your left hand and decrease the pressure with your right.

The bottle will come up again.

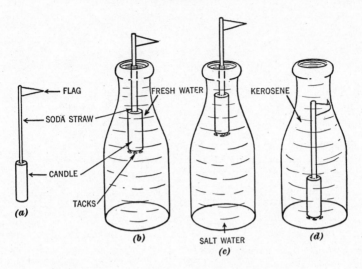

53. A Flag Buoy in Fresh Water, Salt Water, and Kerosene

a. Cut a piece of candle 2 inches long. Soften one end with a lighted match and attach a piece of soda straw 4 inches long.

Slit the upper end of the soda straw and insert a paper flag 1 inch long.

b. Fill a quart milk bottle with fresh water and stick enough tacks into the lower end of the candle to make the buoy sink in fresh water to within 1 inch of the flag.

c. Dissolve four heaping tablespoonfuls of salt in another quart milk bottle of water and put the buoy into this salt water.

The buoy will float higher in the salt water.

Save the salt water for the next experience.

d. Put the buoy into a bottle of kerosene.
It will sink to the bottom.

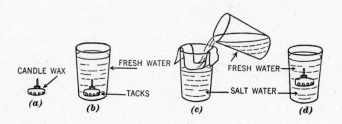

54. A Submarine

a. Cut a piece of candle 1½ inches long, soften it in hot water, and work it into the shape of a submarine. use ¾ inch of a match stick for a periscope.

b. Put the submarine into a tumbler of fresh cold water and add just enough tacks to sink it in fresh water.

c. Fill a tumbler *half* full of strong salt solution and fold a strip of paper down on the salt water to prevent mixing. Fill the tumbler with fresh water and remove the paper carefully.

d. Put the submarine into the tumbler and it will float halfway down.

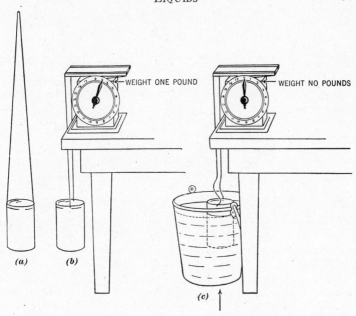

55. A Ship Appears to Have No Weight in Water

a. Let an empty 12-ounce baking-powder can represent the ship. Punch two holes in opposite sides of the upper rim and attach a loop 2 feet long.

b. Suspend the can from a balance and pour in water until the total weight is one pound.

c. Lift a pail of water up under the ship and the ship will appear to have no weight at all.

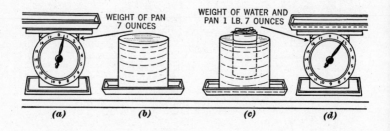

WEIGHT OF PAN
7 OUNCES

WEIGHT OF WATER AND
PAN 1 LB. 7 OUNCES

(a)   *(b)*   *(c)*   *(d)*

56. A Ship Displaces its own Weight of Water

Let the baking-powder can and water of the last experience represent the loaded ship. Their total weight is one pound.

a. Weigh an empty baking pan, or other flat vessel.

b. Stand an empty one-pound coffee can in the pan and fill the can with water until it is heaping slightly.

c. Float the ship in the can and it will displace water.

d. Weigh the pan and water and you will find that the 1-pound ship displaced one pound of water, that is, its own weight of water.

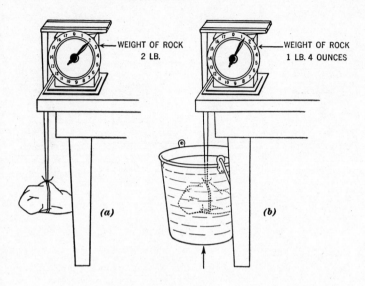

WEIGHT OF ROCK
2 LB.

WEIGHT OF ROCK
1 LB. 4 OUNCES

(a)   *(b)*

57. A Rock Appears to Lose Weight in Water

a. Find a rock weighing about 2 lbs. and of such size that
it will go into a 1-pound coffee can.   Suspend it from
a loop 2 feet long and weigh it.   The rock shown
here weighs 2 lbs. or 32 ounces.

b. Lift a pail of water up under the rock and it will appear
to lose weight.

In this case it weighs only 20 ounces. That is, it appears
to lose 32 − 20 or 12 ounces in weight in water.

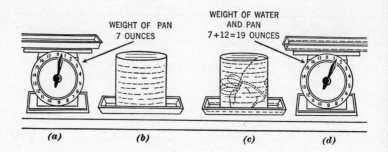

58. A Rock Displaces a Weight of Water Equal to the Weight it Loses in Water

Use the rock of the last experience. In that case it lost 12 ounces in water.

a. Weigh an empty baking pan.

b. Stand a 1-pound coffee can in the pan and fill the can with water until it is heaping slightly.

c. Lower the rock into the can and it will displace water.

d. Weigh the pan and displaced water and you will find that the rock displaces the weight it loses: 12 ounces in this case.

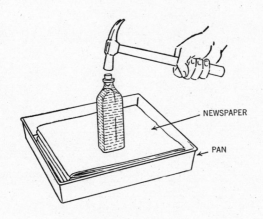

NEWSPAPER

PAN

59. Break a Bottle

Find a bottle with *flat* sides and find a cork stopper of the proper size.   A baby's nursing bottle is excellent.

Fill the bottle with water and insert the stopper without admitting air.

Use a pan to catch the water and place in it a partly unfolded newspaper to serve as a cushion.

Stand the bottle on the newspaper in the pan and hit the stopper with a hammer.

You will be surprised how easily the sides of the bottle break *outward*.

Gather the broken glass in the newspaper and deposit the glass and paper in the ash can.

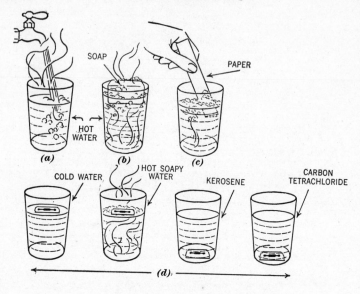

60. Liquid Surfaces, Strong and Weak

a. Fill a tall tumbler to within 1 inch of the top with *hot* water.

b. Place a piece of soap in the hot water for one minute or more.

c. Lift out the soap and remove the bubbles from the surface with a piece of paper.

d. Stand in a row four tumblers filled to the same height respectively, with cold water, hot soapy water, kerosene, and carbon-tetrachloride.

Drop a safety razor blade from a height of about one-fourth inch flat on the surface of each.

The blade will float on the cold water and possibly on the hot soapy water, but it will sink instantly in the kerosene and carbon-tetrachloride.

Rock gently the two tumblers in which the blades are floating. The blade in the hot soapy water will sink first.

Keep the liquids for the next experience.

61. Divers and Liquids

a. Cut four pieces of unglazed newspaper 3″ x 2″.

b. Fold them lengthwise.

c. Cut out as indicated.

d. Put in eyes, nose, and mouth and you have four divers.

e. Drop one head-first into each liquid from a height of about ½ inch.

    The diver in cold water will sink very slowly; the one in hot soapy water, more rapidly; and those in kerosene and carbon-tetrachloride, instantly.

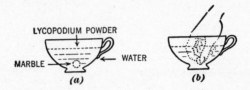

62. To Lift a Marble out of Water without Wetting Your Fingers

a. Place a marble in a teacup, cover it with ¼ to ½ inch of water and sprinkle lycopodium powder over the water to a thickness of about $\frac{1}{16}$ inch. Use plenty.

b. Lift out the marble. Your fingers and thumb will be covered with a layer of powder but they will be dry.

Note. You can buy sufficient lycopodium powder at a drug store for five cents.

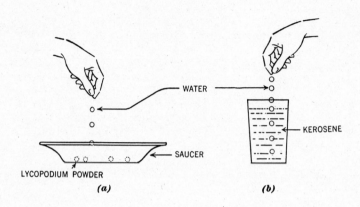

(a)   (b)

63. Water Spheres

a. Sprinkle lycopodium powder over the inside of a saucer to a depth of about $\frac{1}{32}$ inch and sprinkle water
drops from the fingers into the saucer.

The drops will form water spheres which will run
about in a lively manner when you tilt the saucer.

b. Fill a tumbler with kerosene and shake water drops into
it from your fingers.

The small water drops will remain spherical as they
sink through the kerosene.

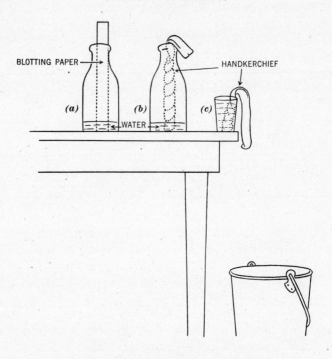

64. Capillarity

a. Stand a strip of blotting paper in an inch of water in a quart milk bottle.

b. Hang a twisted handkerchief in another quart milk bottle, with its lower end dipping into one inch of water.

Examine them after an hour and you will find that water has risen into each to a considerable height.

c. Arrange a handkerchief so that one end is at the bottom of a full tumbler inside and the other *below* the bottom outside.

The handkerchief will empty the tumbler over night.

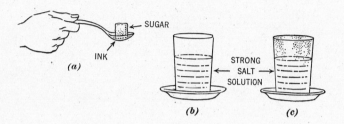

65. Capillarity

a. Place a lump of sugar in a half-teaspoonful of ink.

The ink will rise rapidly in the sugar.

b. Boil a half-tumblerful of water in a sauce-pan and add to it all the table salt it will dissolve and a little more.

When the solution is lukewarm, pour it into a tumbler, place the tumbler in a saucer, and stand it aside for a month or more.

c. The salt will gradually crawl up the inside of the tumbler and down the outside.

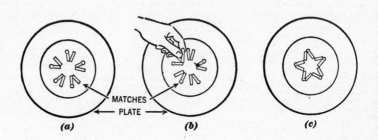

66. A Five-Pointed Star

a. Break five matches half through at the middle and arrange them symmetrically on a dry plate around a circle about ¾ inch in diameter.

b. Dip a sixth match into water and wet each break with a drop or two of water.

c. The matches will form a five-pointed star.

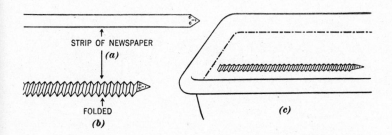

67. A Sea Serpent

a. Cut a 2-inch strip of unglazed newspaper across the full width of the double page.

Make a serpent head with eyes and nose.

b. Fold it back and forth each half inch to make a zig-zag.

c. Fold it tight, place its tail against one side of a bath-tub and release it on water.

The serpent will stretch out quickly across the tub.

d. Make another sea serpent and put it in the bath-tub *on its side.*

It will squirm about in a very realistic manner.

Heat

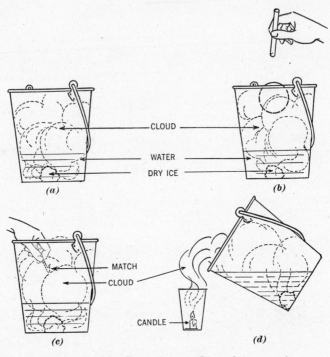

(a)

(b)

CLOUD

WATER

DRY ICE

MATCH

CLOUD

CANDLE

(c)

(d)

68. Dry Ice—Cloud

Warning. Dry ice is very cold, −110° F. Handle it with a teaspoon, not with your fingers.

a. Drop a piece of dry ice into water in a pail.
   A dense white cloud will form in the pail.

b. Drop a soap bubble into the cloud.
   The soap bubble will float in the cloud.

c. Light a match and lower it into the cloud.
   The match will go out.

d. Light a short candle in a tumbler and fill the tumbler with cloud.
   The cloud will pour like a liquid and extinguish the candle.

e. Repeat Experiences 46 and 48 with the cloud.

Why? See page 235

74

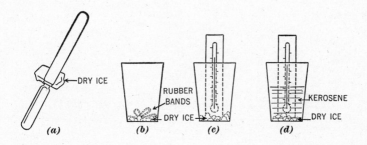

69. Dry Ice—Cooling

a. Press the blade of a dinner knife against dry ice and move it slowly lengthwise.

The blade will cry out and groan.

b. Let rubber bands rest on dry ice in a tumbler for five or ten minutes.

The rubber will lose its elasticity and become brittle.

c. Place a thermometer in a tumbler with dry ice.

It will cool very slowly.

d. Place a thermometer in a half tumbler of kerosene and dry ice.

It will cool more rapidly, but not so rapidly as you would expect.

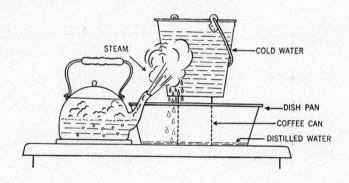

70. To Get Distilled Water for Your Battery

Clean the outside of a pail and a coffee can, then clean
the inside of a dish-pan.

Put a kettle of water over the fire and let the steam strike
the outside of the pail of cold water which stands on
the coffee can in the dish-pan.

The distilled water, condensed steam, will drop into the
dish-pan.

Note.   Renew the cold water about every half hour.

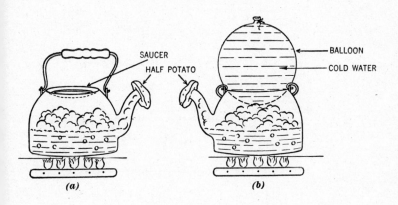

SAUCER
HALF POTATO
BALLOON
COLD WATER

(a)   (b)

71. Steam Pressure Moves the Rattler and Puffing Dancer

a. Shove half of a raw potato over the spout of a tea-kettle and use a saucer instead of the cover.

Get up steam and turn the saucer slowly.

You will find a position where the saucer rattles enthusiastically.

b. Fill a round five-cent balloon with cold water until it is about 1½ inches larger in diameter than the top opening of the kettle. Tie the balloon and use it instead of the saucer.

The balloon will puff and dance merrily.

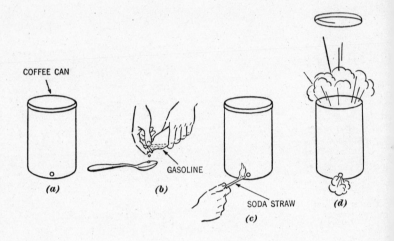

72. Gasoline Engine Power Stroke

a. Punch a hole about $\frac{1}{3}$ inch in diameter in the side of a coffee can near the bottom.

b. Measure five drops of gasoline into a spoon, put the gasoline bottle 10 feet away for safety, drop the five drops of gasoline into the can and put on the cover.

c. Light a soda straw at one end and insert this end into the hole.

d. You will see and hear a loud but safe explosion.

> *Warning.* Gasoline takes fire very easily. Use only a small bottle of it. Keep the bottle corked and keep it a long distance from an open fire.

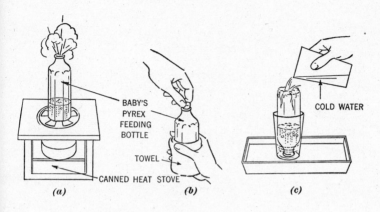

(a)   *(b)*   *(c)*

73. To Boil Water by Cooling It

a. Buy a baby's Pyrex feeding bottle with a sound cork
stopper. Pour hot water into it to a depth of about
1 inch. Boil the water until the steam has issued
for one minute or more.

b. Then take these steps in order:

1. Put out the fire.

2. Put a towel around the bottle, hold it standing on
the table, and insert the cork firmly.

c. 3. To make sure that the stopper will not let in air,
invert the bottle into a small tumbler of water and
stand them in a baking pan or other flat vessel.

4. Pour cold water a little at a time over the bottle,
and the water in the bottle will boil a long time,
although it is getting cooler and cooler.

5. To pull out the cork easily, heat the bottle right
side up in a sauce-pan of boiling water for about five
minutes, lift it out and remove the stopper.

Note. Baby's Pyrex bottles cost 25 cents at a drug store. **Sterno**
stoves cost 10 cents, Sterno Corporation, 9 East 37th Street, New
York City. Sterno cans cost 10 cents each.

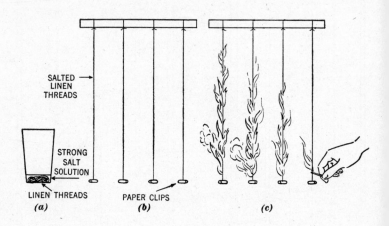

SALTED LINEN THREADS

STRONG SALT SOLUTION

LINEN THREADS
(a)

PAPER CLIPS
(b)

(c)

74. To Support a Weight on a Burned Thread

a. Put a heaping tablespoonful of table salt into a tumbler and wet it with two tablespoonfuls of water.

Cut 4 *heavy linen* threads 18 inches long and soak them in the salt water for five minutes or more.

b. Tie each thread to a support and attach a paper clip, or other light weight, at its lower end. Let the threads dry over night.

c. Light each thread with a match and the burned thread will support the light weight.

Note. The thread must be linen.

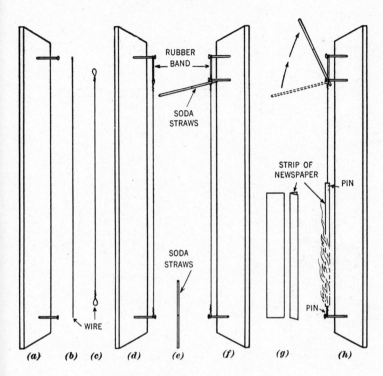

RUBBER
BAND

SODA
STRAWS

STRIP OF
NEWSPAPER

PIN

SODA
STRAWS

PIN

WIRE

(a)   *(b)*   *(c)*   *(d)*   *(e)*   *(f)*   *(g)*   *(h)*

75. The Wire Expands

a. Find a board about 7 feet long, 6 inches wide, and 1 inch thick and drive two 4-inch spikes into it exactly 6 feet apart.

b. Cut a wire exactly 6 feet long.

c. Twist exactly 3 inches at each end into a loop.

d. Put one loop over the lower spike *near its head,* and attach the other loop to the upper spike *near its head* by means of 4 stretched rubber bands.

e. Slit one end of a soda straw for 1 inch and slide this end into the end of another soda straw, to make a light pointer.

f. Drive in a third 4-inch spike in such position that it touches the upper loop and its *under* side is at the *middle* of the loop.   Insert the soda-straw pointer into the loop with the inserted end *under* the spike.

g. Cut a 3-inch strip of newspaper about 3 feet long and fold it lengthwise.

h. Pin the paper around the *lower end* of the wire and light it at its lower end.

You will see the outer end of the pointer rise when the wire is heated and sink when it cools.

i. Test an iron wire and a copper wire at the same time, each wire having its own rubber bands and pointer. Pin the paper around *both* and light it.   The copper will expand and contract more than the iron.

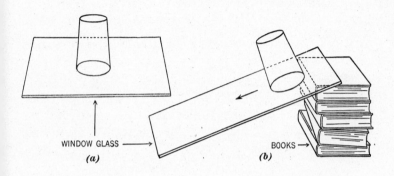

WINDOW GLASS →
(a)

BOOKS →
(b)

76. A Skiing Tumbler

a. Secure a piece of window glass and invert one tumbler after another on it until you find one with a rim that touches the glass at every point.

b. Now tilt the window glass until you reach the angle at which the inverted tumbler is just about to slide but does not do so.

Fill the tumbler with *hot* water, empty it and place it upside down near the high end of the glass.

Presently the tumbler will ski gracefully down the hill.

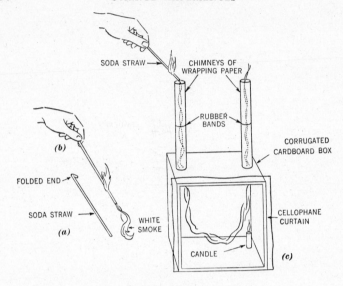

77. Hot Air Convection

a. To make a simple smoke producer, fold over one end of a soda straw for ½ inch.

b. Hold the straw by the folded end and light it 2 inches from the other end.

You will see white smoke issue from the end.

c. To see hot air convection.

1. Find a corrugated card board box about 10″ x 10″ x 10″ and cut away one side.

2. Cut out two 1½-inch circles in the top near opposite sides and fit each with a rolled wrapping paper chimney, held with a rubber band.

3. Fit the front with a cellophane curtain, place a short lighted candle under one chimney and hold a soda-straw smoke producer over each chimney in turn. The curtain must fit airtight.

You will see the smoke move down in the cold-air chimney into the box and up in the hot-air chimney.

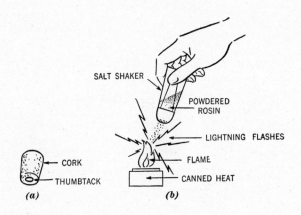

78. Heat and Lightning

a. Heat. Stick a thumbtack with rounded head into one end of a cork and rub it vigorously back and forth on the carpet or floor, then touch it to the back of your hand.

You will find it hot.

b. Lightning. Powder rosin very fine, place it in a salt shaker, and shake it into a flame, preferably in the dark.

You will see bright flashes resembling lightning.

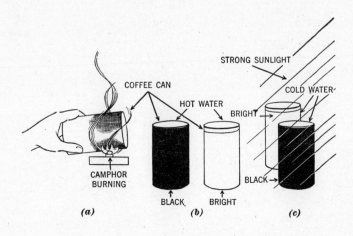

79. Radiation and Absorption of Heat

a. Place a ¼″ x ¼″ x ¼″ piece of camphor on a coffee-can cover, light it, and smoke the outside of a coffee can until it is very black with soot.

b. Stand the black can and a similar bright can side by side in the shade; fill them both with hot water.

Take the temperature of each at once, cover them, and take their temperatures again after about two hours. The black can will cool faster than the bright can.

c. Empty the cans, fill them with cold water, take their temperatures, cover them, and stand them in bright sunlight.

Take the temperature of each again after one or more hours.

The black can will absorb heat faster than the bright can.

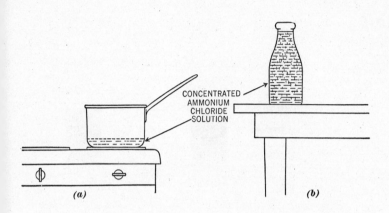

80. Imitation Snow Storm and Two Surprises

a. Fill a quart milk bottle at the *hot-water faucet* to *within 2 inches of the top.*

Pour the water into a sauce-pan, add to it one pound of ammonium-chloride salt, and stir the mixture.

First surprise. Feel the solution and you will find it cold.

Warm the solution *only until it is lukewarm,* stir it until the salt dissolves, and pour it into a quart milk bottle.

Second surprise. The solution now more than fills the bottle.

b. Cap the bottle, rinse it with warm water, dry it, and stand it on a table.

Soon you will see an imitation snow storm in the bottle. It will continue a long time.

When you wish to repeat the snow storm, pour the solution and salt into a sauce-pan, heat it until it is *lukewarm only,* stir it until the salt is dissolved, and pour it back into the bottle.

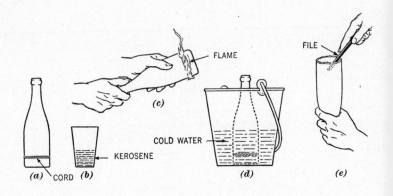

81. To Cut Off the Bottom of a Bottle

a. Use cotton cord between $\frac{1}{16}$-inch and $\frac{1}{8}$-inch in diameter, not twine. Wrap the cord three times around the bottle, leave enough to tie, and cut it.

b. Soak the cord in kerosene for five minutes.

c. Wrap the kerosene soaked cord around the bottle with the loops close together and tie it. Cut off the knot ends.

Hold the bottle nearly horizontal but with the bottom about 2 inches above the top, light the kerosene, and turn the bottle over and over until the flame dies down.

d. Dip the bottom into cold water and hold it there until it is cool. Tap the bottle with a file just below the cord and the bottom will separate.

e. Smooth the sharp edges with a file, outside and inside, just enough to prevent them from cutting you.

The edge will be irregular because most bottles vary in thickness and are imperfectly annealed.

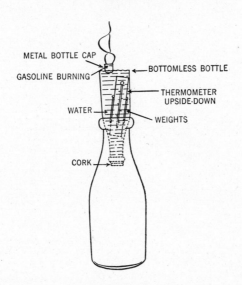

METAL BOTTLE CAP

GASOLINE BURNING

BOTTOMLESS BOTTLE

THERMOMETER
UPSIDE-DOWN

WATER

WEIGHTS

CORK

82. To Show that Water is a Poor Conductor of Heat

Use a bottomless quart soda bottle, close it with a cork, and stand it upside down in a quart milk bottle.

Attach spikes, or other weights, to a short ten-cent thermometer and place it upside down in the bottomless bottle.

Pour cold water into the bottle until the thermometer is covered.

Dig the cork slice out of the metal cap of a vinegar bottle, pour a *half*-teaspoonful of gasoline into the cap, float the cap on the water in the bottle and light the gasoline.

The temperature of the water will change very little if at all.

Note. You can buy ten-cent thermometers at the five and ten-cent stores. Be sure the liquid thread in the stem is not broken.

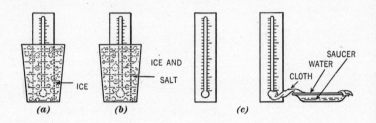

83. Thermometer Experiences

a. *To test your thermometer*. Put it into a tumbler of cracked ice and a little water.

It will register 32° F. if it is accurate.

b. *To find the temperature of ice and salt*. Place the thermometer in a tumbler containing salt and *very finely powdered ice*, mixed in the proportion of 1 salt to 3 ice, by volume.

The lowest possible temperature for the mixture is minus 7.6° F.

c. *Air humidity*. Tie one end of a piece of old handkerchief to the bulb of a thermometer and let the other end dip into a saucer of water.

After the handkerchief and bulb are wet, stand a dry-bulb thermometer near by and fan both vigorously.

The less the difference in temperature the greater the humidity, and vice versa.

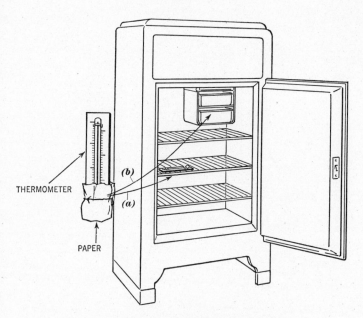

84. To Test Your Refrigerator

a. Wrap the bulb of a dry thermometer in paper to keep
the temperature constant while you read it. Place
the thermometer on the middle shelf and read it
next day. It will read 50° F. or less if your refrig-
erator is up to standard.

b. Place the wrapped thermometer in a dry ice-cube tray
and read it next day. It will read between 5° F.
and 20° F.

Water Pressure[1]

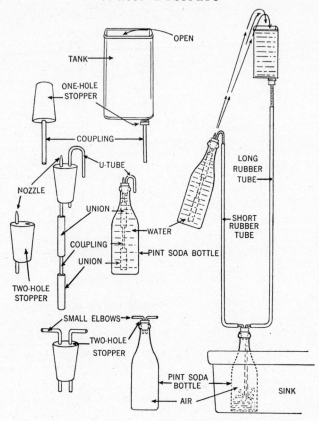

85. Is This Perpetual Motion?

Arrange the equipment as indicated, stand the lower bottle in a sink, fill the tank with water, and hold everything as shown.

You will see the stream of water from the nozzle rise above the water surface in the tank.

Note 1. Always wet glass and rubber before you insert glass into rubber.

Note 2. Always separate glass and rubber as soon as you finish an experience, to prevent them from sticking together.

[1]The equipment needed for these experiences is described on pages 209 to 222.

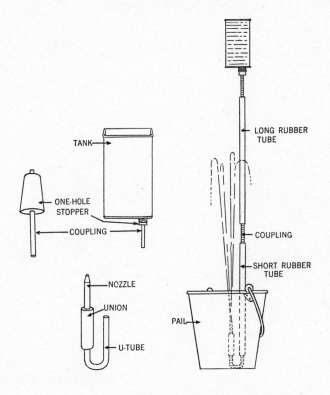

86. A Fountain

Arrange the equipment with the pail on the floor, fill the tank with water, and hold it while standing on a chair.

You will see a fine fountain.

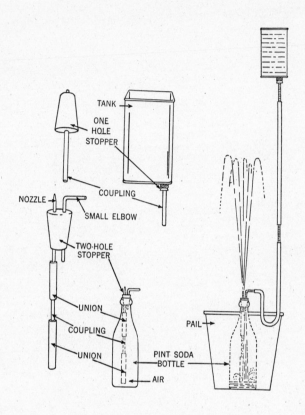

87. Another Fountain

Arrange the equipment with the air-filled bottle in a pail on the floor. Fill the tank with water and hold it up while standing on a chair.

You will see a fine fountain.

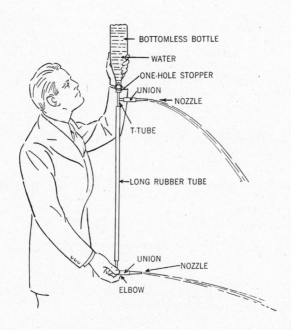

BOTTOMLESS BOTTLE

WATER

ONE-HOLE STOPPER

UNION

NOZZLE

T-TUBE

LONG RUBBER TUBE

UNION

NOZZLE

ELBOW

88. Unequal Streams

Arrange the equipment, fill the bottomless bottle with
water, and hold it as shown. The lower stream will be
longer than the upper stream.

Note. Directions for cutting the bottom from a bottle are given on pages
88 and 220.

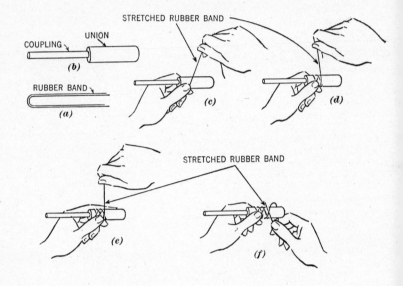

89. A Secure Fastening

In the next experience and in many others you will need
to fasten securely a glass tube in a rubber tube or
rubber balloon. A simple way to do this is by means
of a *stretched rubber band*, as follows:

a. Cut one end of the rubber band.

b. Insert the glass tube into the rubber tube.

c. Hold one end of the rubber band against the rubber
tube *with the left thumb*.

d. *Stretch the band* and wind it *stretched, each turn on
top of the preceding turn.*

e. Extend the left forefinger and wind the last turn over
it.

f. Slip the end under this last turn and pull it through.
This fastening will hold very securely.

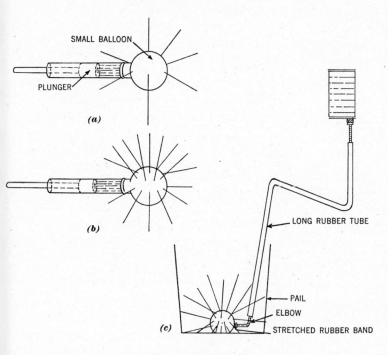

90. Equal Streams

a. Wet one end of the large glass tube and wet the mouth
of a small round one-cent balloon. Pull the balloon
mouth over the end of the tube, fill the tube and
balloon with water, and insert the plunger. Punch
a half dozen pin holes around the equator of the
balloon, fill the tube and balloon again, and drive in
the plunger. The horizontal streams will be of the
same length if the holes are of the same size.

b. Punch holes as shown and repeat.

c. Make this test.

The streams will come out with equal force, and will
be of equal length if the holes are of the same size.

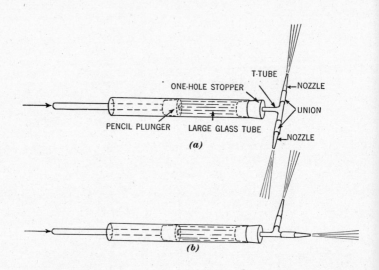

ONE-HOLE STOPPER
T-TUBE
NOZZLE
UNION
NOZZLE
PENCIL PLUNGER   LARGE GLASS TUBE
(a)

(b)

91. Equal Streams

a. Arrange the large glass tube, one-hole stopper, T-tube, plunger, unions, and nozzles, as a syringe.

Fill the syringe with water, hold it with the nozzles at the same level, and shove in the plunger.

The streams will be of equal length, if the nozzle holes are of the same size.

b. Repeat with this new arrangement and the streams will again be of equal length, if the nozzle holes are of the same size.

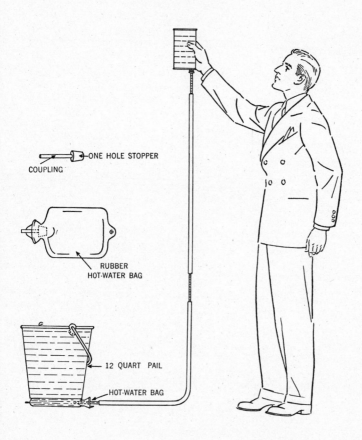

92. A Pint of Water Lifts Twenty Pints

Fill a 12-quart pail nearly full of water and stand it on a
rubber hot-water bag arranged as shown. Hold up the
tank and keep filling it with water.

You will see one pint of water in the tank and tubes lift
the twenty pints of water and the pail.

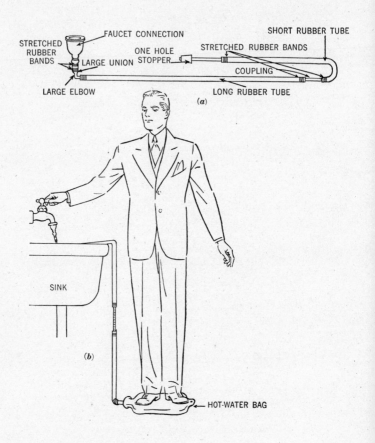

93. The Water Lifts You

a. Arrange the equipment.

b. Connect with a hot-water bag and cold-water faucet.
Stand on the bag and turn on the water.
You will feel yourself being lifted.

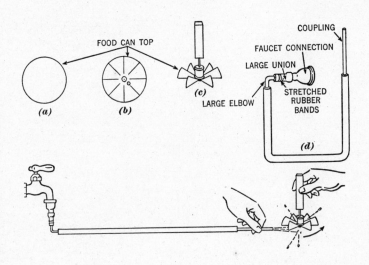

94. A Water Wheel

a. Cut out the top of a large round food can.

b. Punch a large nail hole at the center and a smaller hole near it. Divide the top into eight equal segments.

c. Tack the top to one end of a large spool and nail both loosely to a wooden support by means of a nail smaller around than the hole in the top and spool. Bend the segments to make paddles.

d. Arrange the tubing.

e. Connect with a faucet and turn on the water. The water will spin the wheel merrily.

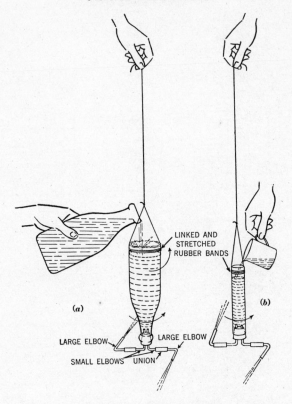

LINKED AND
STRETCHED
RUBBER BANDS

(a)

(b)

LARGE ELBOW   LARGE ELBOW

SMALL ELBOWS   UNION

95. Reaction Turbines

a. Attach a short cord handle to the bottomless bottle by
means of three stretched rubber bands linked together. See Experience 104. Attach a long single
cord to this handle.

Arrange the stopper, unions, and elbows, and fill the
bottle with water.

The reaction turbine will revolve as shown.

b. Repeat with the large glass tube.

The small turbine will revolve more rapidly than the
large one.

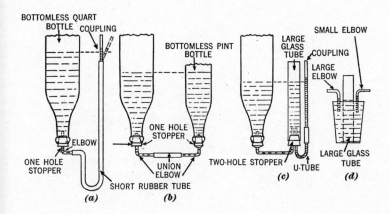

96. Balancing Water Columns

a. b. c. Make the tests and you will find the water columns of the same height, except that the column in the coupling will be about ⅜-inch higher.

d. Capillary rise. Place the glass tubes in a glass of water, dip them below the surface to wet them inside, raise them slightly, hold them in a vertical position, and look at the water levels inside through the side of the tumbler.

You will find the water levels inside higher than the water level in the tumbler about as follows: in the large glass tube ⅛ inch, in the large elbow ¼ inch, in the small elbow ⅜ inch. The higher water levels are due to capillarity.

See also Experiences 64 and 65.

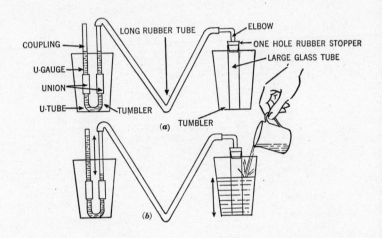

97. The Principle of an Automobile Tank Gauge

a. Set up a U-gauge, fill it *half* full of water and stand it in an empty tumbler. Set up the large glass tube in another tumbler and connect it with the U-gauge.

b. Pour water to a depth of 2 inches into the tumbler holding the large glass tube. The water surfaces in the U-gauge will show a difference in level of 2 inches.

Try with depths of 3 and 4 inches of water.

This principle is applied in gasoline tanks, oil tanks, water tanks, etc., to show at a distant point the depth of liquid in the tank.

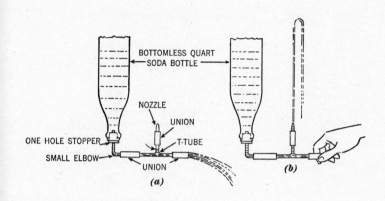

98. Hydraulic Ram

a. Let the water flow from the outlet union and the water level in the side tube will be low.   See arrow.

b. Pinch the outlet union to stop the flow suddenly, and the first spurt from the nozzle will shoot up above the water level in the bottomless bottle.

This illustrates the principle of the hydraulic ram.

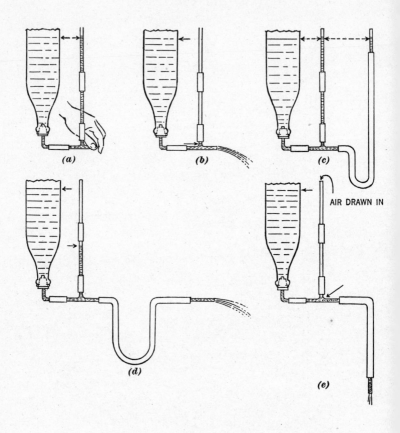

(a)   (b)   (c)

(d)

AIR DRAWN IN

(e)

99. Water at Rest and in Motion

a. The surfaces of the water at rest are at the same level (nearly).

b. The surfaces of the water in motion are not at the same level. See arrows.

c. The surfaces of the water at rest are at the same level (nearly).

d. The surfaces of the water in motion are not at the same level.

e. Water moving rapidly down a vertical tube may draw air in.

See also Experience 96.

Atmospheric Pressure

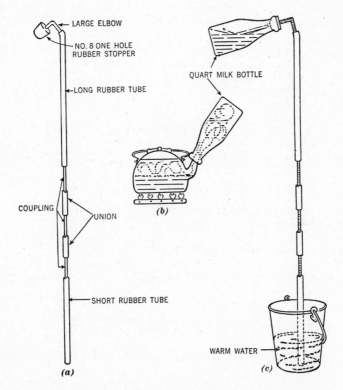

100. Water Runs Up Hill Six Feet or More

a. Arrange the equipment.

b. Steam the inside of a quart milk bottle for one minute.

> *Note:* Pour water into the tea-kettle until the hole leading into the spout is only *half* covered. The steam can then pass through the upper half into the spout and bottle.

c. Fill a pail partly full with *warm water*. Remove the milk bottle from kettle, insert the large stopper into its mouth quickly and raise both, but keep the lower end of the lower tube under water.

Water will run up into the bottle.

Note. Warm water will not crack the hot milk bottle.

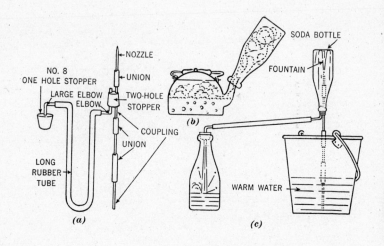

101. A Fountain

a. Arrange the equipment.

b. Steam the inside of a quart milk bottle for one minute and insert the large stopper into it quickly.

c. You will see a fine fountain.

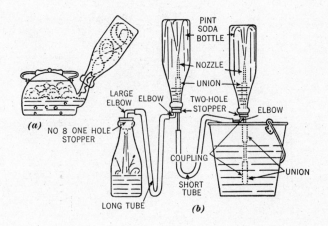

102. A Double Fountain

a. Arrange the equipment as above, steam the inside of
   the quart milk bottle for one minute, and attach it
   as shown.

b. You will see a fine fountain in each bottle.

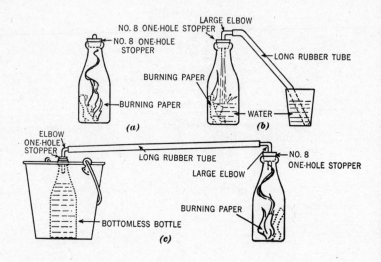

103. Atmospheric Pressure and a Milk Bottle

a. Drop a 4″ x 4″ folded burning paper into the milk bottle and close it with the plugged stopper.

You will find it hard to remove the stopper.

b. Drop a 4″ x 4″ folded burning paper into the empty milk bottle and insert the stopper.

You will see water flow from the tumbler into the bottle.

c. Stand the bottomless bottle in a quart of water in a pail, and make the test indicated.

You will see water rise into the bottomless bottle.

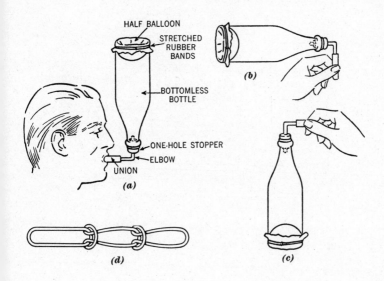

104. Atmospheric Pressure is Equal in All Directions at a Given Point

a. Cut a large round five-cent balloon in two and fasten the bottom half over the bottomless end of a quart soda bottle by means of three stretched rubber bands. Insert the stopper with elbow and union.

Suck out air and the balloon rubber will move into the bottle.

b. Pinch the union and turn the balloon end sidewise; the rubber will remain in the same position.

c. Turn the balloon end downward or in any direction and the rubber will remain in the same position.

d. For the stretched rubber bands, use three uncut bands and loop the end of one into the end of the next to make a row of three fastened together.

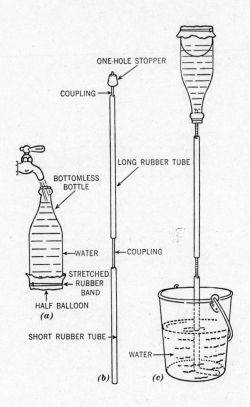

ONE-HOLE STOPPER

COUPLING

LONG RUBBER TUBE

BOTTOMLESS BOTTLE

WATER

COUPLING

STRETCHED RUBBER BAND

HALF BALLOON
(a)

SHORT RUBBER TUBE

WATER

(b)   *(c)*

105. Suction

a. b. c. Fill the bottomless bottle of the last experience with water and make the test. Hold the inverted bottle as high as you can and still keep the end of the lower tube in water.

You will see the balloon rubber stretch down into the bottle.

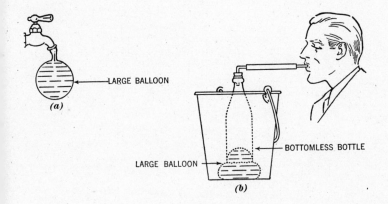

106. To See Suction

a. Fill a large balloon with water and tie it.

b. Place it in a pail, cover it air-tight with the open end of a bottomless bottle, and suck air out of the bottle.

Part of the balloon will be pushed up into the bottle.

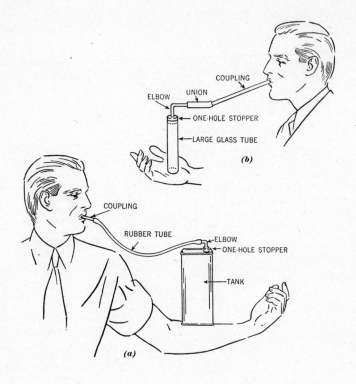

107. To Feel and See Suction

a. *To feel suction,* roll up your sleeve, press the open end of the tank down air-tight on your forearm, and suck air out of the tank.

You will feel the flesh under the tank move up into the tank.

b. *To feel and see suction,* press the open end of the large glass tube air-tight against your palm, and suck air out of the tube.

You will feel and see the flesh under the tube move up into the tube.

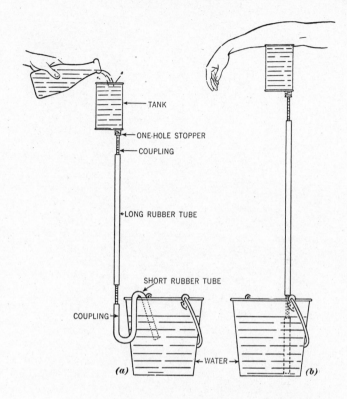

TANK

ONE-HOLE STOPPER

COUPLING

LONG RUBBER TUBE

SHORT RUBBER TUBE

COUPLING

WATER

(a)

(b)

108. To Feel Suction

a. Arrange the equipment.

b. Wet your forearm, press the open end of the tank full of water air-tight against it, stand on a chair, and hold the tank as high as you can and still keep the end of the lower tube under water.

You will feel very strong suction.

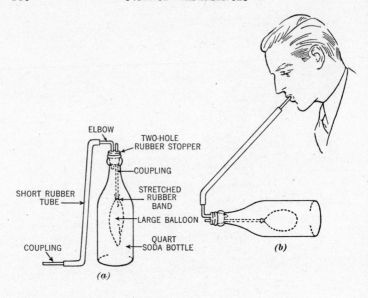

ELBOW
TWO-HOLE RUBBER STOPPER
COUPLING
SHORT RUBBER TUBE
STRETCHED RUBBER BAND
LARGE BALLOON
QUART SODA BOTTLE
COUPLING
(a)
(b)

109. A Respirator

a. Arrange the equipment. The large balloon represents the patient's lungs.

b. Suck air out of the bottle and you will see the balloon expand. Let in air and you will see the balloon (lung) contract and expel air.

The Drinker respirator is an air-tight steel box into which the patient is laid with his head outside at one end. An air-tight rubber collar is then fitted about his neck. The pressure of the air in the box is alternately decreased and increased at the intervals of natural breathing and outside air moves into and out of his lungs as in breathing.

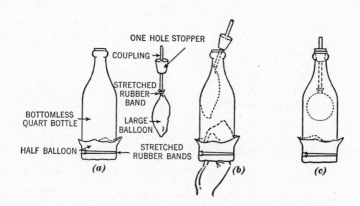

ONE HOLE STOPPER
COUPLING
STRETCHED RUBBER BAND
BOTTOMLESS QUART BOTTLE
LARGE BALLOON
HALF BALLOON
STRETCHED RUBBER BANDS
(a) (b) (c)

110. Diaphragm and Lung

a. To represent the diaphragm, attach the bottom half of a large round balloon to the bottomless end of a quart soda bottle. See Experience 104.

To represent a lung, attach a large balloon to a coupling in a one-hole stopper.

b. Shove the balloon (lung) into the bottle but do not insert the stopper. Force the diaphragm in by hand to expel air from the bottle.

c. Insert the stopper and remove your hand. The diaphragm will sink and the lung will breathe in. Force the diaphragm in again and the lung will breathe out.

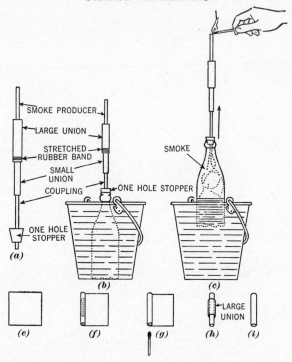

111. The Bottle Smokes

a. Arrange the equipment.

b. Sink the bottomless quart soda bottle in a pail *full* of water and insert the stopper.

c. Hold a lighted match to the smoke producer and raise the bottle fairly rapidly but keep its bottomless end under water.
The bottle will draw in smoke.

d. Remove the stopper and lower the bottle.
The bottle will puff out smoke.

  To make a paper smoke producer.

e. f. Cut a 4″ x 4″ piece of newspaper and roll one edge around a match.

g. h. i. Remove the match. Roll the smoke producer, place it in the large union, and let it unroll to fit the union. Glue the last half inch, roll it, and let it dry over night.

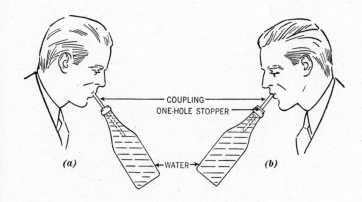

COUPLING
ONE-HOLE STOPPER

(a) ←WATER→ *(b)*

112. You Can and You Cannot

a. You can suck water from the bottle.

b. You cannot suck water from the bottle, if it is *full* of water and *closed* by a one-hole stopper through which the coupling passes.

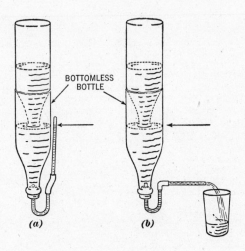

113. A Drinking Fountain

a. Arrange the bottomless bottle and invert into it a whole bottle full of water. The water will stop running when its surface reaches the mouth of the upper bottle.

b. Run water into a tumbler. Air will enter the upper bottle and water will leave it; but the water surface in the bottomless bottle will remain nearly at the level of the mouth of the upper bottle, until the upper bottle is empty.

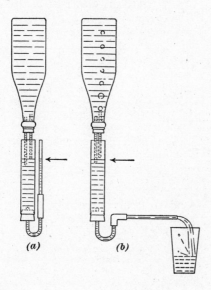

114. Another Drinking Fountain

a. Insert one coupling into a two-hole stopper, and then another about one inch farther.

Fill a bottle with water, close it with the stopper, and invert it over the large glass tube equipped as shown.

Water will run out of one coupling and air will enter the other until the water surface reaches the end of the upper coupling.

b. Pour water into a tumbler, a little at a time. The water surface will move slightly below and above the end of the upper coupling until the bottle is empty.

115. A Trick

a. Put a solid stopper into the lower end of the large glass tube, fill the tube with water and close it with a one-hole stopper.

b. Invert the tube and the water will not run out.

Now seat a friend, hand him the tube, and ask him to remove the solid stopper to smell the mysterious liquid.

He will be surprised to find himself getting wet.

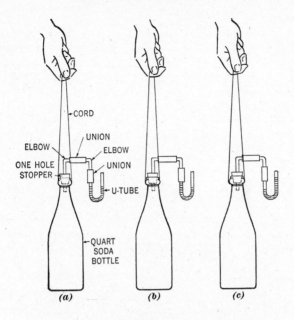

116. Atmospheric Pressure Varies Slowly with the Height

a. Tie a cord to the neck of a quart soda bottle for a handle, to avoid heating the bottle with your hand.

Arrange the one-hole stopper, elbows, unions and U-tube. Fill the U-tube half full of water to serve as a pressure gauge.

b. Carry the bottle downstairs and the water level in the outer arm of the U will sink slightly.

c. Carry it upstairs and the water level will rise slightly.

Better still, ride up and down in an elevator while you observe the water level.

Note. The water in the U-tube will evaporate into the air of the bottle and thereby increase the pressure in the bottle slowly. This will cause a slow rise in the water level of the outer arm of the U.

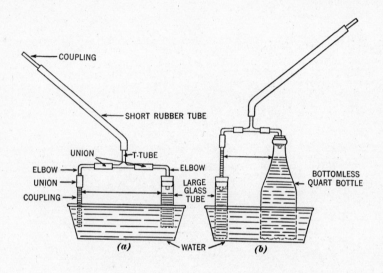

COUPLING

SHORT RUBBER TUBE

UNION — T-TUBE

ELBOW — ELBOW
UNION — LARGE GLASS TUBE
COUPLING —

BOTTOMLESS QUART BOTTLE

(a) WATER *(b)*

117. The Water Columns are the Same Height (Nearly)

a. Arrange the equipment and suck out a little air.

You will find the columns of the same height except that the column in the coupling will be about ⅜ inch higher, due to capillarity. See Experience 96.

b. Repeat with this arrangement.

You will find a similar result.

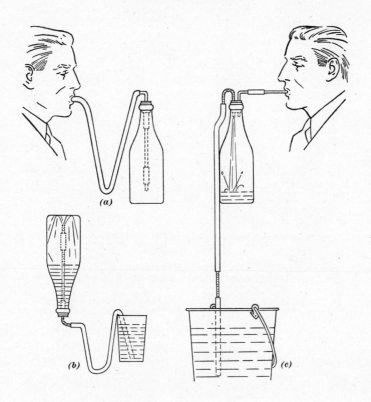

(a)

(b)

(c)

118. To Test Your Suction

a. Suck air out of the bottle, pinch the tube, rest, suck out more air, and repeat until you cannot remove more air.

b. Release the pinched tube under water.

The volume of water which enters equals the volume of air removed.

c. Test how *high* you can suck water.

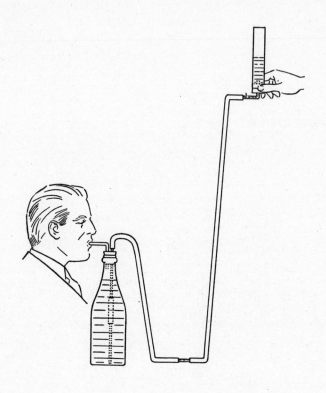

119. To Test Your Lung Force

Blow into the bottle while a friend raises the large glass tube until the water in the tube begins to move downward.

The height in feet from the water surface in the bottle to that in the large glass tube is your lung force in feet of water.

Do not overdo it.   You might injure your lungs.

Siphons

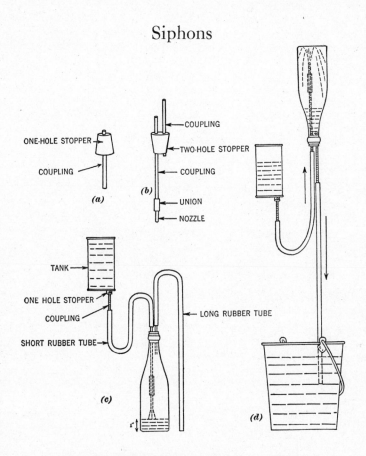

120. The Water Rises Above its Source

a. b. Arrange the equipment.

c. Fill the tank with water and run water into the bottle to a depth of one inch.

d. Invert the bottle above the tank but keep the lower end of its long tube under water in a pail.

You will see a fountain in the bottle although it is above the water level in the tank.

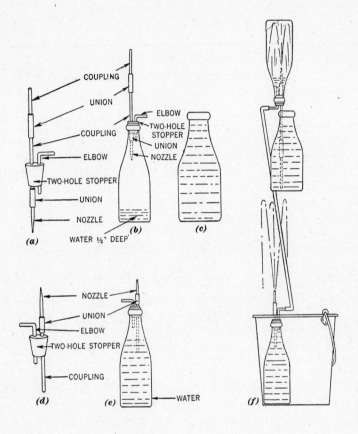

121. Two Fountains

a. b. c. d. e. Arrange the equipment.

f. Invert the upper bottle, put the lower coupling in the milk bottle, and hold them as high as the rubber tubes will permit.

You will see two fine fountains.

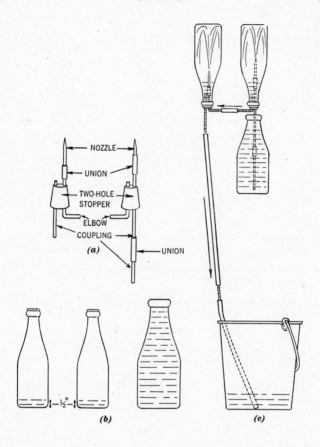

122. A Double Fountain

a. Arrange the equipment.

b. Pour water into the bottles as indicated.

c. Make the test and you will see a fine fountain in each soda bottle.

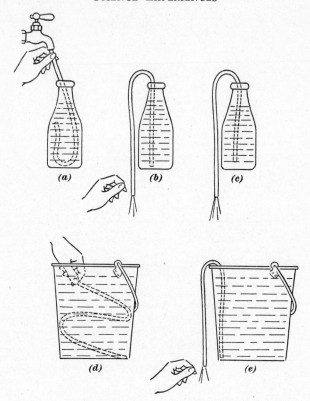

123. Various Ways of Starting a Siphon

To start a siphon, you must fill the tube with the liquid to be siphoned and thereby expel the air from it.

a. Fill the bottle and pinch the end of the tube.

b. Release the end when it is lower than the water surface in the bottle and the water will flow.

c. Suck air from the outer end of the tube when it is lower than the water surface and the water will flow.

d. Sink the tube under water, being sure to keep the part in water lower than the part just entering the water.
Pinch the end and draw the tube partly out of the pail.

e. Release the end when it is lower than the water surface in the pail and the water will flow.

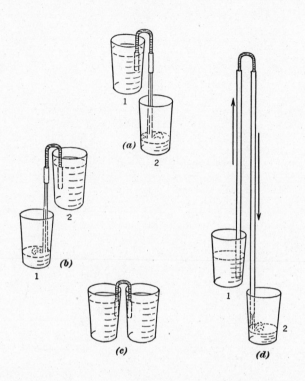

124. Short and Long Siphons

a. Siphon water from 1 into 2.

b. Before the flow stops, lift 2 above 1.

   The water will flow in the opposite direction.

c. Stand the tumblers side by side.

   The flow will stop when the water levels are the same.

d. Repeat a, b, c with the long siphon.

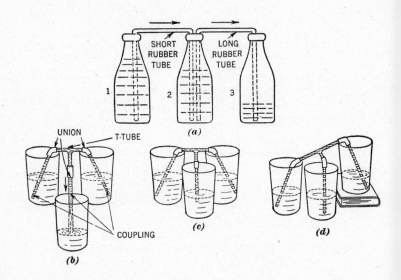

125. A Double Siphon and a Three-Legged Siphon

a. Siphon water from 1 to 2 and from 2 to 3.

The flow is always from the higher to the lower water level and it stops when the water levels are the same.

b. Arrange a three-legged siphon.

c. and *d.* The flow is always from the higher to the lower water level and it stops when the water levels are the same.

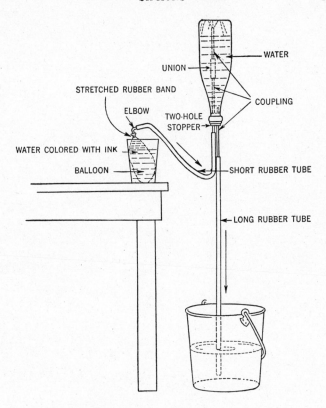

WATER

UNION

STRETCHED RUBBER BAND

ELBOW

COUPLING

TWO-HOLE
STOPPER

WATER COLORED WITH INK

BALLOON

SHORT RUBBER TUBE

LONG RUBBER TUBE

126. An Aspirator

Pour a teaspoonful of ink into a balloon, fill the balloon
   half full of water, and attach an elbow by means of a
   stretched rubber band.   Stand the balloon in a tumbler.

Arrange the equipment, fill the bottle with water and
   invert it.

You will see the aspirator draw the colored water out of
   the balloon.

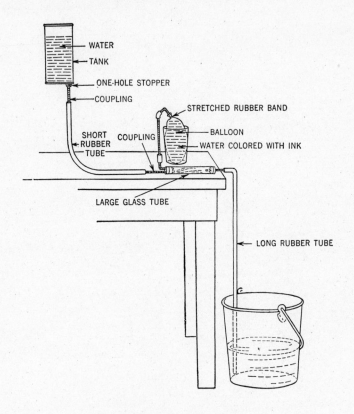

127. Another Aspirator

Prepare the balloon as in the last experience.

Arrange the equipment, run water from the tank into the pail, and then pinch the rubber tube just below the tank.

You will see the aspirator draw the colored water out of the balloon.

128. Air Pressure and Suction

Arrange the equipment.

Fill the upper bottle with water, invert it, and slant it away from its elbow.

Hold your finger near the upper elbow and you feel suction.

Hold it near the lower elbow and you feel air pressure.

Invert the whole equipment when the upper bottle is empty and the lower full, and repeat.

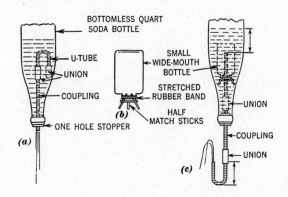

129. Automatic-Discharge Siphons

a. Pour water slowly into the bottomless bottle.

The discharge will start when the U-tube is covered.

b. Attach three half-matches to the neck of a small wide-mouthed bottle, with a stretched rubber band.

c. Pour water slowly into the bottomless bottle.

The first discharge will start when the water is above the upper coupling.

All later discharges will start only when the water is above the upper coupling a distance equal to the depth of the U-tube.

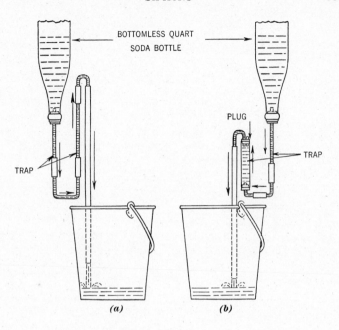

(a)   *(b)*

130. Siphon Traps

a. *Trap with small equal arms.* Pour water into the bottomless bottle.

The trap will be nearly *empty* after the discharge stops.

b. *Trap with large middle arm.* Pour water into the bottomless bottle.

The trap will be nearly *full* after the discharge stops.

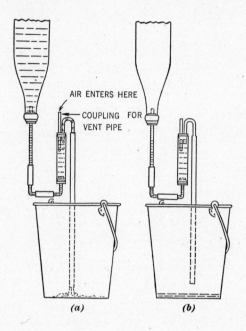

AIR ENTERS HERE

COUPLING FOR
VENT PIPE

(a)   *(b)*

131. A Siphon Trap with a Vent Pipe

a. Pour water into the bottomless bottle and let it discharge.

Air will be drawn in through the vent pipe.

b. After discharge the trap will be nearly *full* of water.

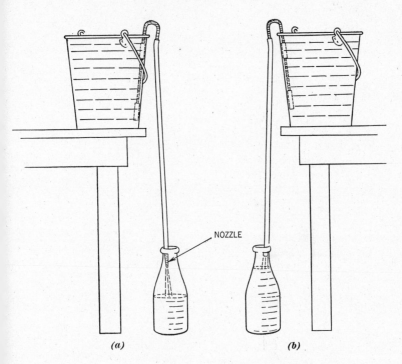

NOZZLE

(a) *(b)*

132. The Smaller the Nozzle the Less the Flow

a. Arrange the equipment with a nozzle.   Suck air out of
   the nozzle to start the siphon and measure the flow
   in one minute.

b. Repeat with the end of the rubber tube for a nozzle.
   The flow will be greater.

   The smaller the nozzle the smaller will be the flow,
   for the same head and time.

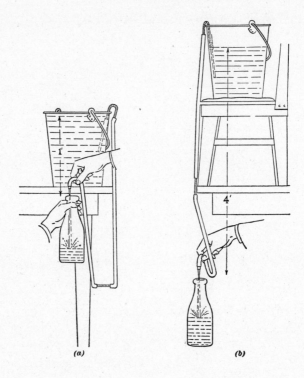

(a)   (b)

133. Four Times the Height Doubles the Flow

a. Arrange the equipment, start the siphon, and let it run until all the air is out of it. Hold the nozzle outlet just one foot below the water surface in the pail and run the water into the bottle exactly one minute. Stand the bottle aside.

b. Use the same equipment but hold the nozzle outlet exactly 4 feet below the water surface in the pail. Run the water for exactly one minute into a similar bottle.

Compare the amounts and you will find that the water in bottle *b* is twice that in *a*.

That is, you must quadruple the height to double the flow of the water.

Air, Compressed and Expanded

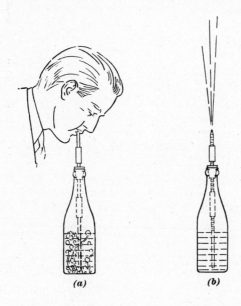

(a)   (b)

134. A Fountain

a. Fill a pint soda bottle half full of water, insert the nozzle, unions, couplings, and one-hole stopper, then blow as hard as you can to force air into the bottle.

b. Jump back quickly and you will see a fine fountain.

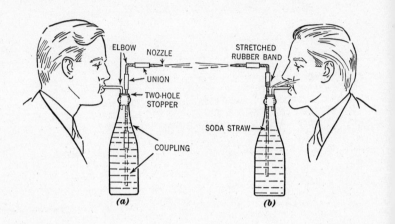

(a)   *(b)*

135. Squirt Bottles

a. Fill the bottle with water and blow hard into the elbow. You will produce a fine stream.

b. *Trick squirt bottle.* Use a soda straw as shown and cut a small hole near its upper end. Hold a finger over the hole and blow a long stream in front of a friend who does not know about the hole.

He will wish to try. Let him do so and tell him to blow hard. He will be surprised to find his face getting wet.

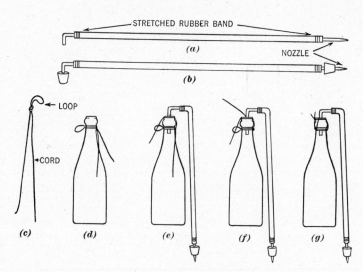

136. To Arrange a Pneumatic Tank

a. b. Arrange the equipment.

c. Cut a 26-inch length of stout cord, double it, and tie a half-inch loop in the doubled end.

d. Pass the halves two and a half times around the neck of the bottle and tie them in a firm double knot *exactly opposite* the loop.

e. Insert the elbow stopper firmly into the mouth of a quart soda bottle, then pass one-half the cord around the elbow and through the loop.

f. Pass the other half of the cord around the elbow in the opposite direction but do not pass it through the loop.

g. Tighten the two cords and tie them firmly above the stopper to hold the stopper securely in the mouth of the bottle.

See the next experience for the use of this pneumatic tank.

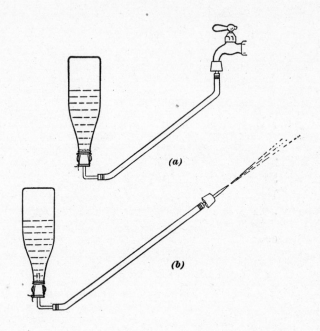

137. To Use the Pneumatic Tank

a. Let a friend hold the bottle *upside down* while you insert the end of the nozzle into the mouth of a water faucet and hold the nozzle stopper firmly against the mouth of the faucet.

Turn on the water and fill the bottle *not more than half full* of water. Squeeze the rubber tube.

b. Go to a place where you have a long range, point the nozzle at an upward angle, and release the tube.

You will see the water shoot twenty feet or more.

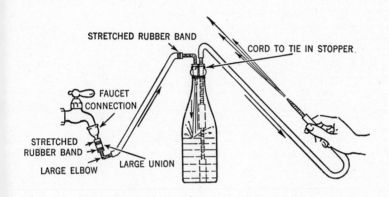

STRETCHED RUBBER BAND

CORD TO TIE IN STOPPER.

FAUCET CONNECTION

STRETCHED RUBBER BAND

LARGE ELBOW   LARGE UNION

138. Air Chamber

Arrange the equipment and be particular about the stretched rubber bands (see Experience 89) and the cord to tie in the stopper (see Experience 136).

Run water into the bottle and you will get a fine stream which will continue after you shut off the faucet.

Warning. Do not let the water rise above the middle of the bottle, because the air pressure in the bottle increases very rapidly above this point.

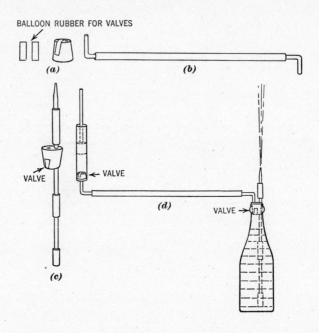

139. An Air Pump

a. Cut two pieces of balloon rubber about $\frac{3}{8}''$ x $2''$ for valves and place one over one hole of a two-hole stopper at the small end.

b. Fasten an elbow in each end of a rubber tube.

c. Arrange one two-hole stopper with a valve and tubing for the bottle.

d. Arrange the second two-hole stopper with a valve in a pump. Fill a quart soda bottle with water, arrange the equipment and pump air into the bottle.

You will produce a fine fountain.

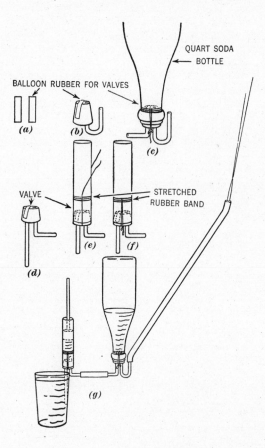

140. A Force Pump

a. Cut two strips of balloon rubber about ⅜″ x 2″ for valves.

b. Place one strip over one hole of a two-hole stopper at the small end and insert an elbow and U-tube into the holes at the other end.

c. Tie the stopper securely into the mouth of a pint soda bottle as explained in Experience 136.

d. Place the other strip of balloon rubber over one hole in another two-hole stopper and insert a coupling and elbow into the stopper.

e. To tie this stopper into one end of the large glass tube, pull a stout cord over the stopper, and clamp the cord to the large tube with a stretched rubber band, then:

f. Tie the ends of the cord firmly under the stopper.

g. Arrange the equipment, move the plunger up and down vigorously, and you will produce a fine long stream.

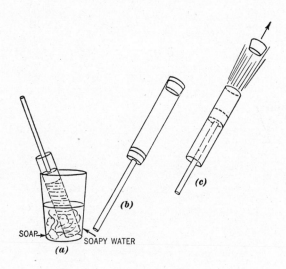

141. A Pop-Gun

a. Put a piece of soap into a tumbler half full of water and put the large glass tube into the soapy water. Move the plunger up and down to clean the tube and to make it slippery.

b. Insert the solid stopper into one end of the tube and the plunger into the other.

c. Shove the plunger in hard and the solid stopper will shoot out with a loud pop.

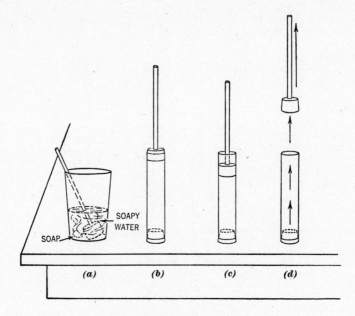

142. A Pop-Up Gun

a. Rinse the plunger in soapy water.

b. Hold the large glass tube upright with the solid stopper resting on the table and insert the plunger into its upper end.

c. Shove the plunger down quickly.

d. Release it quickly, and it will shoot up to the ceiling.

There is a knack to this. The secrets of success are:

1. Don't let air escape from the tube when you insert the plunger. If it does, *remove the plunger,* wet it, and try again. Expand or contract the plunger if need be.

2. Keep the plunger slippery with soapy water.

3. Shove the plunger down only about one inch until you learn the knack of it.

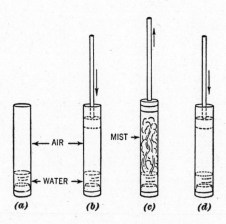

143. Mist

a. Insert the solid stopper into the lower end of the large glass tube and pour in about one-half inch of water.

b. Insert the plunger and shove it down.

c. Release the plunger and you will see thin mist form in the tube. You will see this best if you work with your back to the light.

d. Shove the plunger down again and the mist disappears. Release it and the mist re-appears.

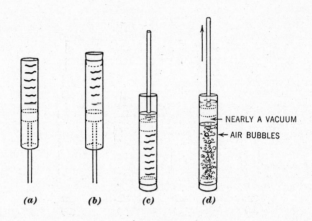

(a)   (b)   (c)   (d)

144. To Pump Air Out of Water

a. Shove the plunger half-way into the large glass tube and fill the space above it with water.

b. Insert the solid stopper without admitting air.

c. Invert the tube and pour water in above the plunger to make it air-tight.

d. Hold the tube and raise the plunger. You will see thousands of air bubbles come out of the water below the plunger.

Release the plunger and you will see only a small air bubble beneath the plunger.

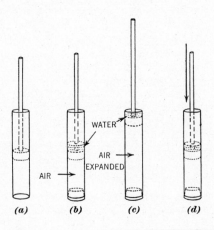

145. Expanded Air

a. Shove the plunger half-way into the large glass tube.

b. Insert the solid stopper into the lower end and pour water above the plunger to make it air-tight.

c. Hold the tube and raise the plunger.

d. Release the plunger and it will shoot back down the tube.

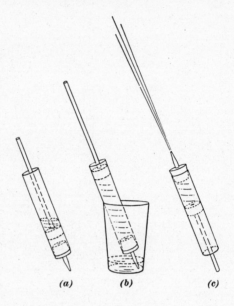

(a)   (b)   (c)

146. A Syringe

a. Insert a one-hole stopper and nozzle into one end of the large glass tube and the plunger into the other. Pour a little water above the plunger to make it airtight.

b. Dip the nozzle into water, raise the plunger, and water will fill the tube.

c. Point the nozzle upward and shove in the plunger. You will produce a fine long stream.

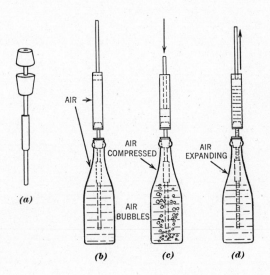

147. You Appear to Change Air Into Water

a. Pass a wet coupling through two wet one-hole stoppers and attach a union and coupling below.

b. Fill a pint soda bottle three-fourths full of water and arrange the syringe.

c. Hold down the bottle stopper and shove the plunger down to force air into the bottle.

d. Release the plunger and it will be raised by the water which will fill the syringe.

Note. The plunger must be slippery.

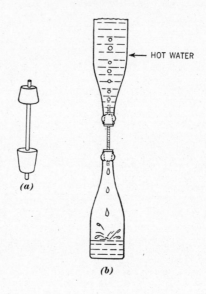

148. A Hiccup Bottle

a. Pass a wet coupling through two wet one-hole stoppers making sure that its ends project slightly.

b. Connect a bottomless bottle with a whole bottle of the same size, pour *hot* water into the bottomless bottle and give the equipment a slight jerk upward.

The equipment will hiccup until the bottomless bottle is empty.

Now invert the equipment over a pail and it will hiccup until it is empty.

Note. You use hot water because it flows through the narrow coupling more readily than cold water. It is much more fluid than cold water.

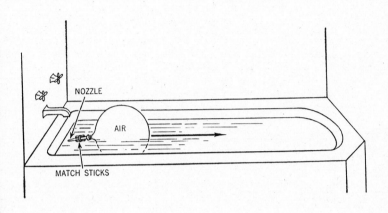

149. A Compressed-Air Boat

Fasten a nozzle in the mouth of a balloon with a stretched rubber band.

Fasten two match sticks to the nozzle with a stretched rubber band in such a way that the nozzle will be nearly horizontal and just under the water surface.

Blow up the balloon and place it on the water in a bathtub.

The compressed-air boat will sail ahead with a put-put sound.

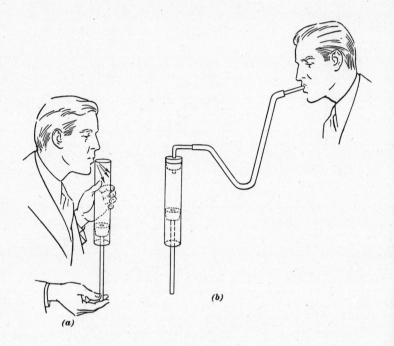

(a)   *(b)*

150. Diablo Whistle and Air Control

a. ***Diablo whistle***. Wet the plunger with soapy water to make it slippery. Blow hard across the top of the large glass tube and move the plunger up and down.

You will produce weird sounds of varying pitch.

b. ***Air control***. Suck out air and the plunger will move up. Blow in air and the plunger will move down.

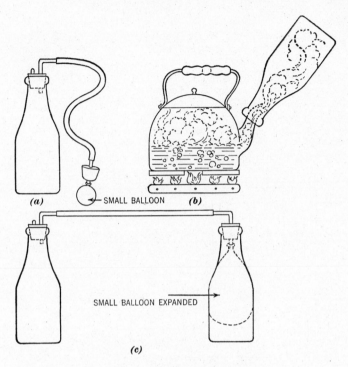

SMALL BALLOON

(a)　　　　　　(b)

SMALL BALLOON EXPANDED

(c)

151. The Balloon Expands

a. Pass the two large elbows through the two No. 8 stoppers and connect them with a rubber tube. Put the plug into the extra hole of the two-hole stopper and insert this stopper into the mouth of a quart milk bottle. Attach a small one-cent balloon to the other elbow below the stopper by means of a stretched rubber band.

b. Steam the inside of another quart milk bottle for one minute.

c. Quickly insert the balloon and its stopper into the mouth of the steamed milk bottle.

The balloon will expand slowly until it nearly fills the milk bottle, unless it bursts.

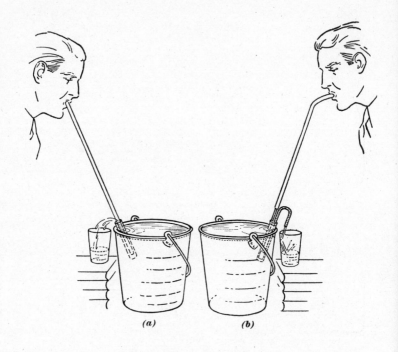

(a)   *(b)*

152. Air-Lift Pumps

a. Place a rubber tube in the large glass tube and hold it
   with its lower end about three-quarters of an inch
   above the lower end of the glass tube.

   Place both in a slanting position in a pail nearly *full*
   of water and blow hard into the rubber tube.

   Water will rise in the glass tube and issue from the
   top in large gobs.

b. Arrange the equipment with the lower end of the union
   about ¾ inch above the lower end of the large glass
   tube and blow into the rubber tube.

   The water will rise in the glass tube and issue from the
   U-tube in spurts.

Other Gases

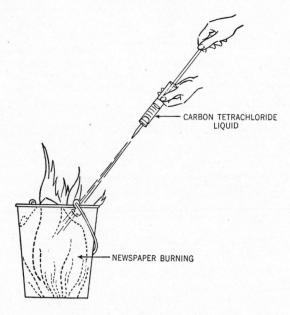

CARBON TETRACHLORIDE
LIQUID

NEWSPAPER BURNING

153. Carbon-Tetrachloride Fire Extinguisher

Make a syringe and fill it with carbon-tetrachloride liquid.

Crumble a single sheet of newspaper in a large pail and light it at the lower side.

When it is burning full blast, squirt carbon-tetrachloride liquid into the pail and the fire will go out.

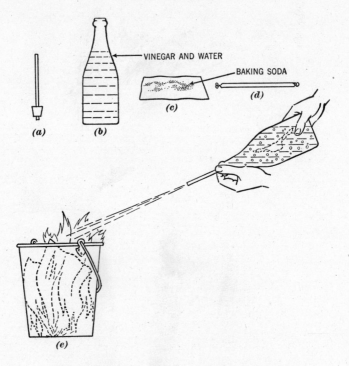

154. Soda-acid Fire Extinguisher

a. Insert a coupling into a one-hole stopper.

b. Fill the body (not the neck) of a pint soda bottle with a mixture half vinegar and half water.

c. Spread a *level* tablespoonful of baking soda on a single sheet of toilet paper.

d. Make it into a long slender roll and twist its ends.

e. Crumble a single sheet of newspaper in a large pail and light it at the bottom.

When the flame is at its highest drop the roll into the bottle, insert the stopper and coupling, and shake the bottle vigorously to break up the paper roll.

Point the resulting stream at the fire and extinguish it.

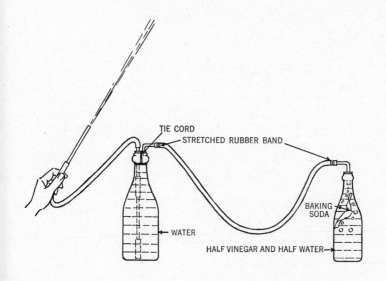

TIE CORD
STRETCHED RUBBER BAND
BAKING SODA
WATER
HALF VINEGAR AND HALF WATER→

155. Soda-Vinegar Fire Extinguisher

Arrange the equipment.

Fill the quart soda bottle with water and tie in the two-hole
  stopper as in Experience 136.

Fill the pint soda bottle as in Experience 154, and shake it
  vigorously.

You will see a fine stream.

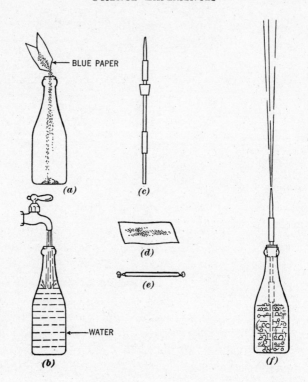

BLUE PAPER

(a)

(c)

(d)

(e)

WATER

(b)

(f)

156. A Seidlitz-Powder Fountain

Seidlitz powders cost five cents each and each consists of two powders wrapped in blue and white paper respectively.

a. Pour the powder from the blue paper into a pint soda bottle.

b. Fill the bottle with water to the bottom of the neck and shake it vigorously to dissolve the powder.

c. Arrange the one-hole stopper, couplings, unions, and nozzle.

d. Spread the powder from the white paper on a *single* sheet of toilet paper.

e. Make it into a thin roll with twisted ends.

f. Stand the bottle in the sink, drop in the roll, insert the stopper, etc., and twist it in very firmly.

Shake it vigorously and you will soon see a splendid fountain.

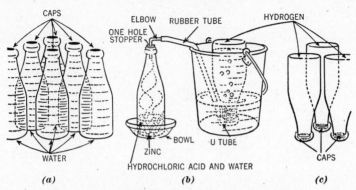

157. To Fill Bottles with Hydrogen

a. Fill six quart milk bottles with water and cap them.

b. Arrange the one-hole rubber stopper, elbow, rubber tube, and U-tube.

Invert a full milk bottle in 3 inches of water in a pail, remove the cup under water, and insert the U-tube.

Cut the zinc casing of a ten-cent flash-light battery into slices which will go into a pint soda bottle. Clean the slices thoroughly.

Pour into the pint soda bottle 2 ounces of strong hydrochloric acid and add 2 ounces of water.

Drop all the zinc into the bottle.

Insert the stopper and collect the hydrogen in the milk bottles.

c. Cap the bottles and stand them upside down on the table.

You will get 5 or 6 quarts of hydrogen.

You can prepare the hydrogen also as described in Experiences 43 and 44.

Warning. Buy the 2 ounces of strong hydrochloric acid at the drug store and *handle it with the greatest care. Do not get any on your hands or clothes.*

Rinse out everything when you have finished.

Note. If you wish to keep hydrogen in an inverted bottle over night, leave a half inch of water in the bottle to cover the cap.

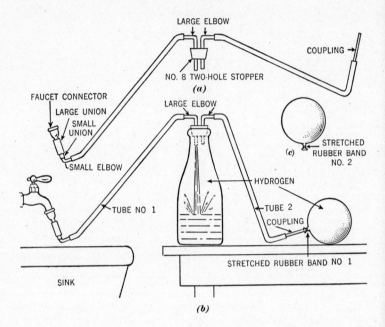

158. To Fill a Balloon with Hydrogen

a. Arrange the equipment.

b. Attach a small one-cent balloon to the coupling with stretched rubber band No. 1.

Bring a quart bottle of hydrogen from the last experience, turn it mouth down, remove the cap, insert the No. 8 stopper, and turn the bottle right side up.

Turn on the faucet and fill the bottle with water to *within one inch of the mouth and* thereby force hydrogen into the balloon.

Let one experimenter pinch tube 2 to keep the hydrogen in the balloon while a second experimenter inserts the No. 8 stopper into a second up-side-down bottle of hydrogen. Force this quart of hydrogen into the balloon and then another—3 quarts in all.

c. Close the balloon with stretched rubber band No. 2. Undo band No. 1 and release the balloon.

It will float up to the ceiling.

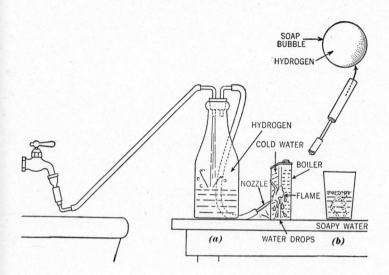

159. Experiences with Hydrogen

a. Hydrogen burns and produces water. Use the equip-
    ment of the last experience but use a nozzle instead
    of the coupling.

Turn on the water, light the hydrogen, and let the flame
    strike the boiler filled with cold water.

You will see the water drops produced by the flame.

b. Hydrogen bubbles float.   Substitute a bubble blower
    for the nozzle and blow a hydrogen bubble.

The hydrogen bubble will float.

c. Hydrogen bubbles burn.   Light a soda straw at one
    end and touch it to a floating hydrogen bubble.

The hydrogen bubble will burst into flame.

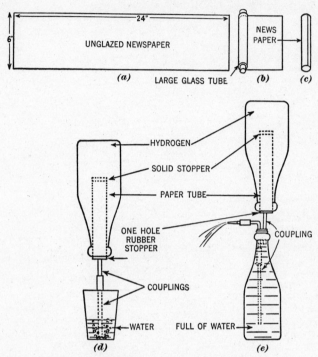

160. Diffusion of Hydrogen

a. Cut a piece of ordinary unglazed newspaper 24″ x 6″.

b. Roll it around the large glass tube.

c. Slide out the glass tube, glue the paper tube, and let it dry over night.

d. Arrange the equipment and invert a quart milk bottle of hydrogen over the paper tube.   Bubbles will appear in the water for a short time.

Remove the hydrogen bottle. Water will rise in the coupling for a short time.

e. Repeat with this equipment.

Water will squirt out of the nozzle for a short time when the hydrogen bottle is placed over the paper tube.

Bubbles of air will enter the nozzle and bottle for a short time when the hydrogen bottle is removed.

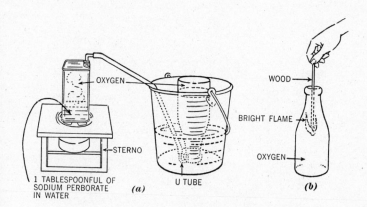

161. To Make and Test Oxygen

a. Measure one level tablespoonful of sodium perborate and put it into the boiler one-third full of water. Arrange the equipment and boil the water.

You will get about one quart of oxygen.

Cap the bottle and place it on the table.

b. Light a splinter of wood at one end, let a good red live coal form, blow out the flame, and plunge the live coal end into the oxygen.

The live coal will burst into a brilliant flame.

Blow out the flame and repeat.

Rinse out the boiler thoroughly.

Note. You can buy ¼ lb. of sodium perborate at a drug store for twenty-five cents.

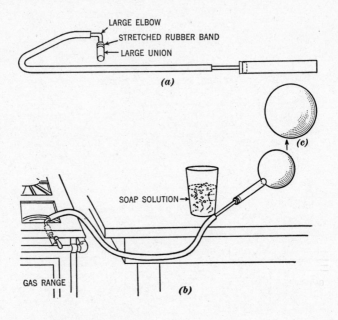

162. Bubbles Filled with Fuel Gas Float and Burn

a. Arrange the tubing.

b. Remove a burner from a gas range, shove the large union over the spud, dip the large glass tube into the soap solution, turn on the gas, and blow a bubble.

c. Detach the bubble and it will float.

d. Light one end of a soda straw and touch it to a detached bubble. The gas will burn.

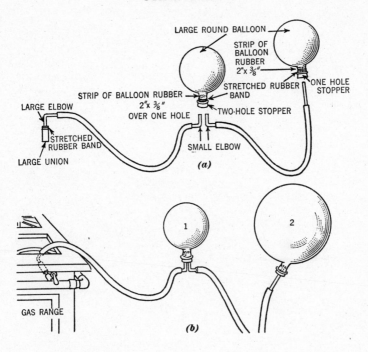

163. To Fill a Balloon with Fuel Gas

a. Arrange the tubing, stoppers, balloons, and particularly the strips of balloon rubber for valves.

b. Turn on the gas, let balloon 1 fill, then squeeze it and force the gas into balloon 2.

Do this time after time until balloon 2 is *very full,* then tie it and detach it.

The balloon will float, if it is very full.

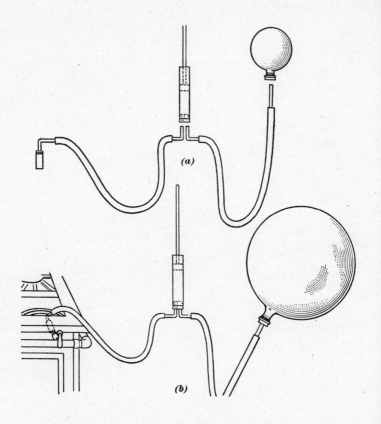

(a)

(b)

164. Another Way to Fill a Balloon with Fuel Gas

a. Repeat the last experience but use the large glass tube and plunger instead of balloon 1.

b. Move the plunger up and down and you will fill the balloon with gas.

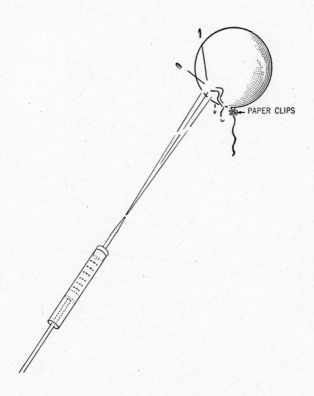

PAPER CLIPS

165. To Shoot Down a Balloon

Attach paper clips to the balloon until it is just floating and shoot it with a stream of water.

The balloon will sink to the floor and rise again after the water on its surface has evaporated.

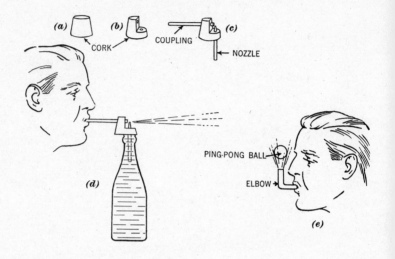

166. Bernoulli Effect with Air

Atomizer.

a. Find a large cork.

b. Cut it into an L-shape and make a hole in each arm of the L.

c. Insert a coupling and nozzle in such a way that the nozzle opening is opposite the *middle* of the coupling opening.

d. Fill a bottle *full to the top* with water, insert the nozzle, and blow *hard*.

The air stream will produce a fine spray.

Ping-pong ball.

e. Blow *hard* into the elbow.

The air stream will support the ball.

See also Experiences 1 to 10 and 14 to 16.

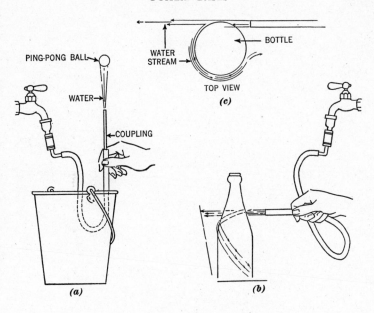

167. Bernoulli Effect with Water

a. The water stream will keep the ball bobbing up and down.

b. The water stream, which strikes one edge of the bottle, divides. Part of it goes straight ahead but part of it clings to the bottle and passes almost completely around it.

c. Top view.

See also Experiences 11 to 13.

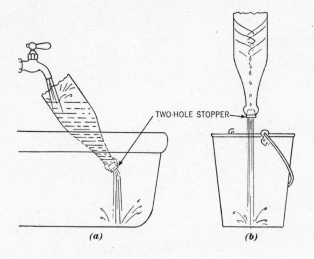

TWO-HOLE STOPPER

(a)   *(b)*

168. A Whirlpool

a. Close the mouth of a bottomless quart soda bottle with a *two-hole* rubber stopper.

Hold the bottle under a wide-open faucet in such a way that the water whirls rapidly as it fills the bottle.

b. Hold the bottle at eye level over a pail—and you will see a fine whirlpool.

Repeat and sprinkle lycopodium powder on the water.

You will see the whirlpool suck the powder down.

LIQUIDS

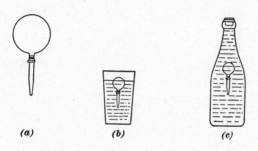

(a)   *(b)*   *(c)*

169. A Diver

a. Fasten a glass nozzle into the mouth of a small one-cent balloon by means of a stretched rubber band.

b. Place this diver in a tumbler of cold water and adjust the air in it until it floats with the top of the balloon about ¼ inch above the water surface.

c. Put a finger over the nozzle outlet and transfer the diver carefully to a quart soda bottle *full* of water, insert a solid stopper hard and the diver will sink. Raise the stopper a little and the diver will rise.

You can startle friends who do not know the trick.

Point your right hand at the diver, look at him hard, and command him to dive or rise, while your left hand unobstrusively presses or releases the stopper.

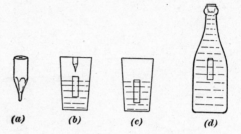

170. Another Diver

a. Cut off one inch of the pointed end of a round lead pencil.

b. Hold a rubber union half submerged in a tumbler of water to let water into the lower half. Insert the pencil into the top of the union to hold air in the upper half.

c. Release the diver and it may float with its head about ⅛ inch above the water surface. If not, adjust the amount of water and air in it until it does float.

d. Put a finger over the lower end of the union and transfer the diver carefully into a quart soda bottle *full* of water. Shove a solid stopper down hard and the diver will sink. Release the stopper and it will rise.

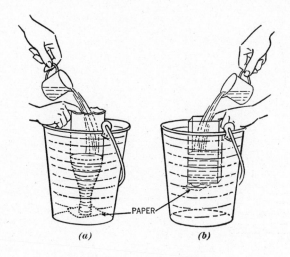

PAPER

(a)   *(b)*

171. A Patch on a Boat

a. Hold a piece of paper over the mouth of the bottomless bottle while you sink the bottle and paper in
water.

The paper illustrates a patch placed over the outside
of a hole in a boat, it holds on and keeps the water
out of the bottle.

Pour water into the bottle and the paper will hold on
until the water level is the same inside and outside
of the bottle.

b. Repeat the experience with the tank.

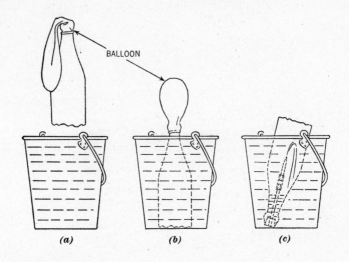

BALLOON

(a)   *(b)*   *(c)*

172. Upward Pressure

a. Blow up a balloon to stretch it, then let out the air and pull its wet mouth over the wet mouth of a quart bottomless bottle.

The balloon will droop.

b. Sink the bottle in a large pail *full* of water and the balloon will expand.

c. Remove the balloon and close the mouth of the bottomless bottle with a one-hole stopper, coupling, union, and nozzle.

Sink the bottle mouth down in a large pail *full* of water and you will see a small fountain.

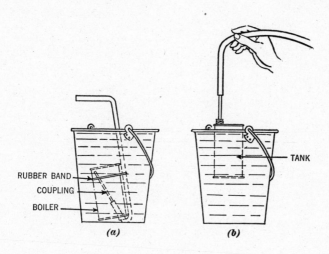

RUBBER BAND

COUPLING

BOILER

TANK

(a) *(b)*

173. Pontoons

a. Arrange the boiler upside down as shown in a pail *full* of water.

Suck out air and the boiler will sink.

Blow in air and the boiler will float.

The rubber band holds the rubber tube against the outside of the boiler and thereby holds the coupling in the boiler.

b. Repeat with the tank arranged as shown.

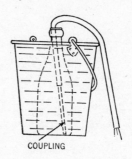

COUPLING

174. The Bottle Rises to the Surface

Fill a quart soda bottle with water, sink it in a pail full
of water but keep its mouth above water. Place in it the
long rubber tube with a coupling at one end.

Siphon water out of the bottle and it will shortly rise to the
surface.

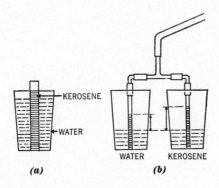

(a)   (b)

175. The Liquid Levels are not the Same

a. Fill a tall tumbler with water nearly to the top, place the large glass tube in the tumbler, and pour kerosene into the tube.

The surface of the kerosene will be higher than that of the water.

b. Pour an inch of water into one tumbler and an inch of kerosene into another.

Arrange the equipment, suck a little air out, and pinch the rubber tube.

The kerosene will rise to a greater height than the water.

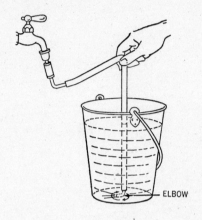

176. The Wiggler

Turn the water on full and the elbow will wiggle around
violently.

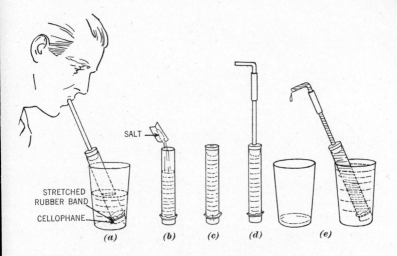

SALT

STRETCHED
RUBBER BAND

CELLOPHANE

(a)   *(b)*   *(c)*   *(d)*   *(e)*

177. Osmosis with Salt

a. Wet a piece of cellophane and fasten it over one end of the large glass tube by means of a stretched rubber band. Place the cellophane under water and blow gently into the tube to make sure there are no holes.

b. Fill the tube half full of water and add one heaping teaspoonful of salt.

c. Fill the tube with water to the very top and twist in the one-hole stopper, being careful to let the excess water escape through the hole.

d. Twist in a coupling with union and elbow.

e. Rinse the outside of the tube and place it in a tumbler of fresh water.

Water will rise slowly in the tube and fill the coupling, union, and elbow. Next day you will find salt water or dry salt in the second tumbler.

> *Note.* Use the kind of cellophane in which candy is wrapped, not that in which cigarettes are wrapped. Much of the latter is made water-proof with paraffin.

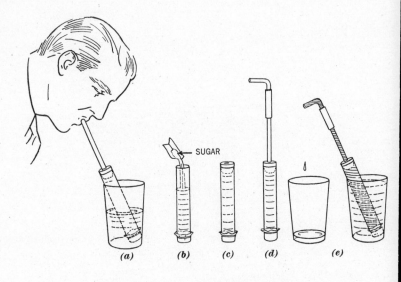

SUGAR

(a)   (b)   (c)   (d)   (e)

178. Osmosis with Sugar

Repeat Experience 177 step by step, but use sugar instead of salt.

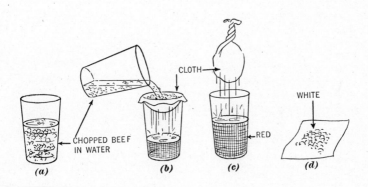

179. To Get Beef Juice by Osmosis

a. Buy a quarter pound of chopped red rare beef, place it in a half tumbler of water, and stir it from time to time during one hour.

b. Strain the liquid through a cloth.

c. Twist the cloth to squeeze out the last drops.

d. Open the cloth and examine the beef.

The beef juice will move into the water and leave the beef white or nearly so.

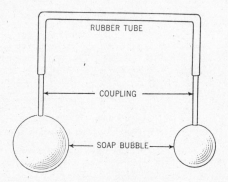

180. The Little Bubble Forces its Air into the Large One

Insert a coupling into a rubber tube and let one experimenter blow a soap bubble about 1½ inches in diameter.

Pinch the rubber to prevent the bubble from contracting.

Let another experimenter blow a soap bubble about 1 inch in diameter on another coupling and insert the coupling into the other end of the tube.

Release the pinched rubber and the smaller bubble will contract and force its air into the larger bubble.

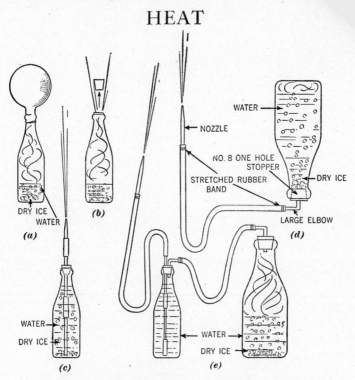

181. Dry-Ice Pressure

a. Drop a half-dozen pieces of dry ice into water in a pint soda bottle and pull the *wet* mouth of a small balloon over the wet mouth of the bottle. The balloon will expand.

b. Insert a solid rubber stopper into the mouth of the bottle.

The stopper will be driven out with a loud pop.

Warning 1. Do not shove the stopper in too firmly or the bottle may explode.

Warning 2. Never try to confine dry ice. Its gas exerts a pressure of over 1,000 lb. per sq. in. at ordinary temperatures and it will burst anything except a strong steel tank.

c. Make the test and you will see a vigorous fountain.

d. You will see a fine fountain.

e. You will see a fine fountain.

See also Experiences 68 and 69.

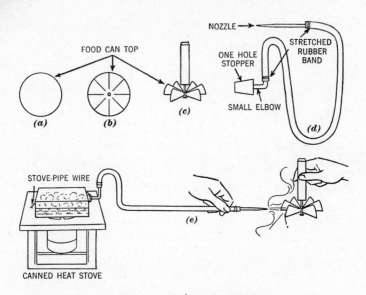

182. A Steam Turbine

a. Cut the round top out of a tin food can.

b. Punch a nail hole at the exact center and cut eight radial slits to within one-half inch of the hole.

c. Attach the turbine to a wooden support by means of a nail smaller than the hole. Bend each section to make the blades of the turbine.

d. Attach an elbow and a nozzle to a long rubber tube by means of stretched rubber bands and insert the elbow into a one-hole stopper.

e. Fill the boiler *half full* of water. Insert the stopper firmly and *fasten it securely* by means of a 20-inch length of stove-pipe wire. Pass the wire once or twice around the elbow, then around the end of the boiler, and twist its ends together.

Get up steam and let it strike the rim of the turbine. It will spin the turbine at very high speed.

Warning. Do not use too much heat. Too great steam pressure might burst the boiler.

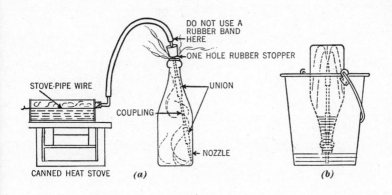

DO NOT USE A
RUBBER BAND
HERE

ONE HOLE RUBBER STOPPER

STOVE-PIPE WIRE

UNION

COUPLING

NOZZLE

CANNED HEAT STOVE *(a)* *(b)*

183. A Fountain

a. Arrange the equipment, but do not use a rubber band
   on the rubber tube just above the bottle stopper.
   Steam the inside of the quart soda bottle for one
   minute, with the stopper *outside* the bottle.

b. Pour *warm* water into the pail and quickly (1) put out
   the fire; (2) insert the stopper; (3) detach the tube
   and (4) invert the bottle into the water in the pail.

   You will see a vigorous fountain in the bottle.

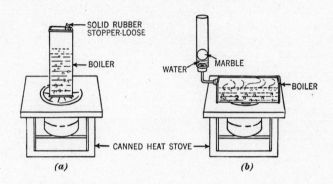

184. The Principle of the Steam Engine

a. Fill the boiler *half full* of water, get up steam, and place the solid rubber stopper *loosely* in the mouth of the boiler.

The stopper will bob up and down in a lively manner.

b. Find a marble that will just go into the large glass tube, the snugger the better as long as it will move.

Get up steam, and you will see the marble bob up and down as soon as a little steam condenses to water between it and the tube.

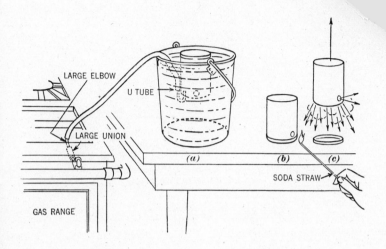

185. The Principle of the Gas Engine

a. Punch a half-inch hole in the side of a coffee can, just under the cover.

Place the uncovered can in a pail of water, fill it with water, turn it mouth down and pass fuel gas into it until it floats *with the bottom about ¾ inch above water*. Shut off the gas.

Raise the can slowly up-side-down to let air in and water out.

b. Put on the cover, stand it top-down on the table, and insert the lighted end of a soda straw into the hole.

c. The can will soar upward.

Note 1. To get gas into the can you may need to raise the can and U-tube because the gas pressure is equal to only about 3 inches of water.

Note 2. Do not use too much gas. If you do it will merely burn without exploding.

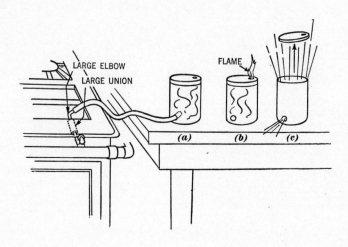

186. A Gas Explosion

a. Punch a hole in the side of the coffee can about one-half inch above the bottom and large enough to admit one end of the long rubber tube. Punch a similar hole in the cover.

Pass gas into the covered can until it has driven out the air.

b. Shut off the gas, withdraw the tube, light the gas, and wait for the explosion.

c. It will come in two or three minutes when the flame ducks under the cover.

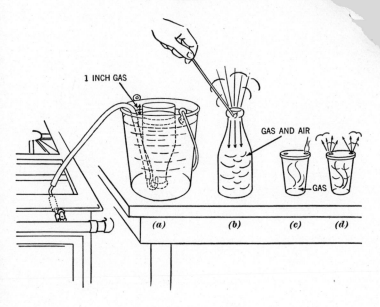

187. Other Gas Explosions

a. Fill a milk bottle with water, cap it, invert it in water, remove the cap, insert the U-tube, and pass in gas *only until it fills one inch.*

Lift the bottle out slowly to let in air slowly and cap it up-side-down.

b. Light a soda straw, remove the cap, and light the gas.

You will see and hear a loud explosion.

See Notes 1 and 2, Experience 185.

c. Fill a tumbler with water, invert it in water, fill it *completely* with gas, and cover it up-side-down with a coffee can cover in which you have punched two *half-inch holes.*

Turn the can right side up and light the gas at *one* hole.

d. You will see and hear a mild explosion.

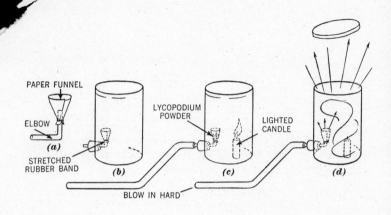

188. A "Dust" Explosion

a. Make a small paper funnel and fasten it to one arm of an elbow with a stretched rubber band.

b. Wet the outside of the other arm of the elbow, pass it out through the hole inside the coffee can, and shove it through a one-hole stopper.

c. Attach the rubber tube, fill the funnel with lycopodium powder, and place a lighted candle in the can.

d. Place the cover on the can and quickly blow in hard.

You will see and hear a fine explosion.

Note. Use a larger can if you can find one. The explosion will be much more impressive, and equally safe.

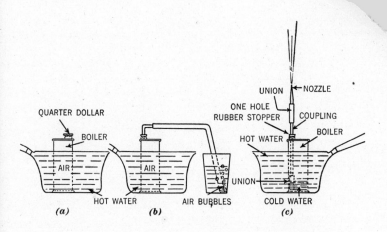

189. Air Expands when Heated

a. Wet a quarter dollar thoroughly with saliva, place it over the mouth of the boiler, and lower the bottle into hot water.

The quarter dollar will "click," "click."

b. Cool the boiler, arrange the equipment, and lower the boiler into hot water.

You will see many air bubbles.

c. Fill the boiler one-third full of cold water, arrange the equipment, and lower the boiler into hot water.

You will see a fine cold-water fountain.

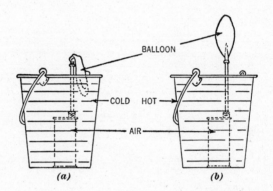

190. The Balloon Shrinks and Swells

a. Fasten a small stretched one-cent balloon to one end
of a coupling with a stretched rubber band. Insert
the coupling into a one-hole stopper and the stopper
into the empty boiler.

Hold the boiler in cold water and the balloon will
shrink.

b. Hold the boiler in hot water and the balloon will swell.

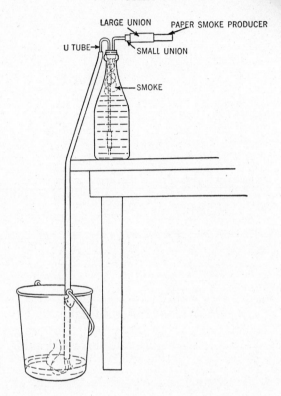

191. To Fill a Bottle with Smoke

Make a paper smoke producer as in Experience 111.

Fill the bottle with water, start the siphon, and hold a
lighted match at the end of the paper.

You will see the bottle fill with smoke to the end of the
siphon in the bottle.

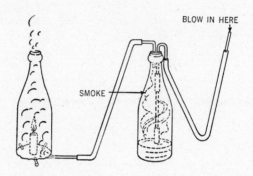

192. Convection in Air

Fill a bottle with smoke as in Experience 191 and arrange the rubber tubing as shown.

Place a lighted candle in a bottomless bottle and support the bottle a little above the table on three match sticks.

Blow smoke gently under the bottle and you will see a strong upward current of smoke and air in the bottle. Try to blow smoke gently down into the mouth of the bottle.

You will again see a strong upward current.

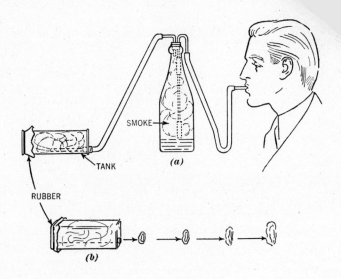

SMOKE

TANK

(a)

RUBBER

(b)

193. Smoke Rings

a. Fasten a half balloon over the open end of the tank
with a stretched rubber band and *fill* the tank with
smoke.

b. Tap the balloon rubber gently.

You will produce a beautiful smoke ring at each tap.

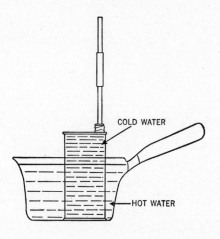

194. Water Expands When Heated

Start water boiling in a saucepan.

Fill the boiler with cold water, insert a one-hole stopper into its mouth, then twist a coupling into the stopper and add a union and second coupling.

Place the boiler in the boiling water. You will see water rise slowly up through the couplings and overflow at the top.

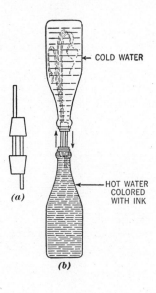

← COLD WATER

(a)

← HOT WATER
COLORED
WITH INK

(b)

195. Convection in Water

a. Join two wet couplings and two wet two-hole stoppers in such a way that one coupling projects beyond each stopper.

b. Pour two tablespoonfuls of ink into a quart soda bottle and fill the bottle with *hot* water.

Fill another quart soda bottle with cold water without ink, close it with the coupled two-hole stoppers, and invert it over the hot bottle.

A stream of colored water will rise into the upper bottle.

FAINT MIST

196. Mist

Wet the inside of a quart soda bottle with water.

Arrange the equipment, turn your back to the light, and suck air out of the bottle.

A faint mist will appear in the bottle.

Let in air and the mist will disappear instantly.

Suck out air and the mist will appear again.

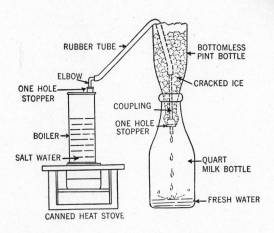

197. To Get Fresh Water From Salt Water

Put two tablespoonfuls of table salt into a tumbler of water and stir it.

Pour the salt water into the boiler until it is half full.

Arrange the equipment and boil the water.

Taste the water in the milk bottle and you will find it free from salt.

It is distilled water.

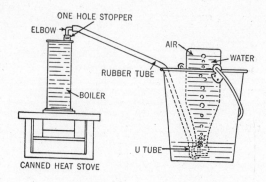

198. To Measure the Air in Drinking Water

Fill the pint boiler to the very top with cold drinking water.

Fill a pint soda bottle with cold water and invert it in water in a pail.

Arrange the connecting tubes and light the burner. Run the test until you hear the cracking of steam bubbles at the mouth of the U-tube.

The air from the pint of water in the boiler will accumulate in the pint soda bottle.

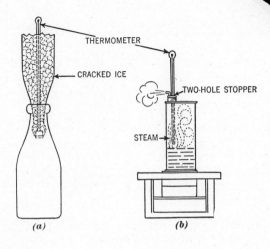

THERMOMETER

CRACKED ICE

TWO-HOLE STOPPER

STEAM

(a)   *(b)*

199. To Test a Laboratory Thermometer

a. Stand it in cracked ice.

It will register 32° F. if it is accurate.

b. Place the bulb in the steam of boiling water, as shown.

The thermometer will register 212° F. at sea level, if it is accurate.

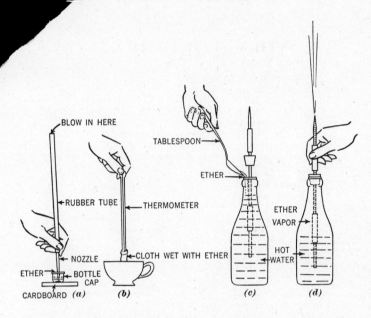

BLOW IN HERE

TABLESPOON

ETHER

RUBBER TUBE — THERMOMETER

ETHER VAPOR

NOZZLE

CLOTH WET WITH ETHER

HOT WATER

ETHER — BOTTLE CAP

CARDBOARD *(a)* *(b)* *(c)* *(d)*

200. Experiences With Ether

a. To make ice. Remove the cork layer from a metal bottle cap, fill the cap half full of ether, stand it on five drops of water on wood or cardboard, and blow until the ether is all evaporated.

You will find the cap frozen to the wood or cardboard.

b. A low temperature. Tie a piece of old handkerchief to the bulb of a thermometer and wet it with ether.

You will see the thermometer register a low temperature.

c. Vapor pressure. Fill a pint soda bottle with *hot* water, arrange the equipment, pour in a tablespoonful of ether, and quickly insert the stopper.

You will see a fine fountain.

Note. You can buy a ¼-pound can of ether for 35 cents.

Warning. Ether is very inflammable. Do not use it within 20 feet of a naked flame, and keep it corked.

YOUR EQUIPMENT

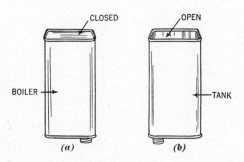

1. Boiler and Tank

a. The boiler is a pint rectangular or cylindrical metal can with a screw top ¾-inch *inside* diameter.

This screw top holds all No. 2 rubber stoppers.

b. The tank is a similar can with the bottom cut out.

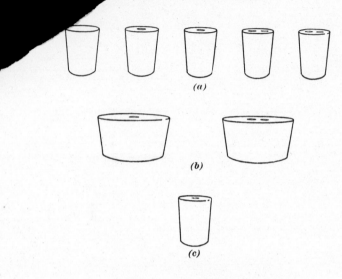

(a)

(b)

(c)

2. Rubber Stoppers

a. Five rubber stoppers, size No. 2, one solid, two with one hole and two with two holes.

These fit the boiler, tank, large glass tube, all soda and vinegar bottles with crimp metal caps, and many common bottles.

Their holes fit No. 2 glass tubing.

b. Two rubber stoppers, size No. 8, one with one hole and one with two holes.

These fit pint and quart milk bottles and their holes fit the plug and the large elbows.

c. One rubber stopper with one hole to be used for a plunger. The size is either No. 0 or No. 1 according to the inside diameter of the large glass tube. See also Your Equipment 10.

Note. Buy the best rubber stoppers. They do not stick so tightly to glass tubing as do cheap stoppers.

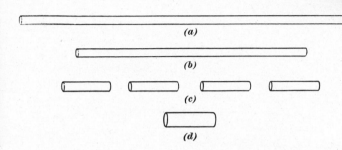

(a)

(b)

(c)

(d)

3. Rubber Tubing

a. Long rubber tube, No. 2, 30 inches long.

b. Short rubber tube, size No. 2, 20 inches long.

c. Four rubber unions, size No. 2, 2 inches long.

These fit all couplings, elbows, nozzles, the U-tube, the T-tube, and the plug.

d. One large rubber union, size No. 4, 2 inches long. This fits air-tight over the rubber tubes and the unions and also over a smoke producer.

Note. Buy the best rubber tubing. It does not stick so tightly to glass tubing as does cheap rubber tubing.

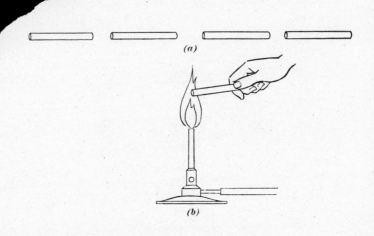

(a)

(b)

4. Glass Couplings

a. Cut four pieces of No. 2 glass tubing, 5½ inches long.

b. Smooth each end by turning it in a Bunsen flame, *above the green cone,* until it begins to be red. These fit the long rubber tubes, the unions, and the holes in the No. 2 rubber stoppers.

> *Note.* The end of a glass tube will contract if you heat it too long. If this happens let the end cool, shorten it ¼ inch, and anneal it again.

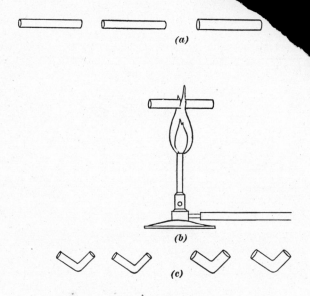

(a)

(b)

(c)

5. Small and Large Glass Elbows

a. Cut four pieces of glass tubing 3 inches long, two from No. 2, and two from No. 4 glass tubing. Smooth the ends as in the previous experience.

b. Turn each in a Bunsen flame above the green cone until it is soft, and

c. Bend it at right angles.

The small elbows fit the holes in the No. 2 stoppers, the large, those in the No. 8 stoppers.

Both fit the rubber tubes and unions.

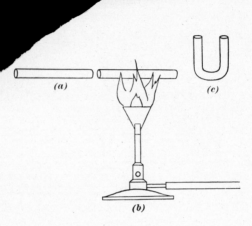

6. Glass U-Tube

a. Cut a piece of No. 2 glass tubing 5 inches long and smooth its ends.

b. Turn it in the flame of a fish-tail burner until it is soft, then

c. *Remove it from the flame* and bend its ends *upward.*

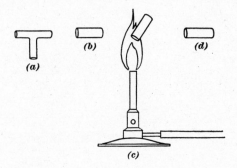

7. Glass T-Tube and Plug

a. Buy a T-tube made of No. 2 glass tubing.

b.. To make a plug, cut a piece of No. 4 glass tubing 1½ inches long and smooth one end.

c. Turn the other end in a Bunsen flame above the green cone until it is entirely closed.

d. This plug fits the holes in the No. 8 rubber stoppers.

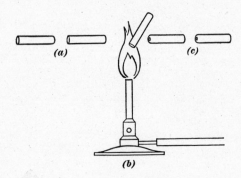

(a)   (c)

(b)

8. Glass Nozzles

a. Cut two pieces of No. 2 glass tubing 2 inches long and smooth one end of each.

b. Turn the other end of each in a Bunsen flame until it is *nearly* closed, and

c. You have two nozzles with small but strong jet ends.

Note. Examine all the glass pieces you have made. If you find an end that has contracted, cut it off ¼ inch and anneal it again. This does not apply of course to the small end of the nozzles or the closed end of the plug.

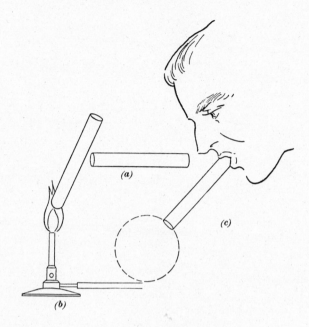

9. Large Glass Tube

a. Cut a piece of No. 10 glass tubing 6½ inches long and smooth its ends. No. 10 tubing is ⅝ inch inside diameter.

b. If your laboratory has no No. 10 tubing, find a test tube 6 inches by ⅝ inside, and heat the closed end very hot.

c. Blow very hard into the test tube to make a large thin glass balloon.

Break away the thin glass and smooth the rough edge in the flame. The resulting large glass tube is only about 5½ inches long but it will serve.

d. You can buy the glass cylinder of a battery hydrometer for 5 cents at a ten-cent store. These are excellent.

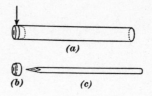

10. The Plunger

a. Put a No. 1 rubber stopper into one end of the large glass tube but do not press it in. Cut it off about ¼ inch beyond the end of the glass tube.

b. Bevel the cut-off end with a pair of scissors.

c. Insert the pointed end of a lead pencil into the hole at the small end of the stopper and twist it in to enlarge the stopper until it fits the large glass tube air-tight.

> *Note.* If the rubber stopper is of just the right size, do not cut or trim it, of course.

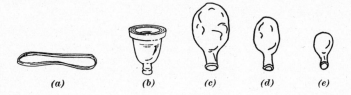

(a)   *(b)*   *(c)*   *(d)*   *(e)*

11. Miscellaneous

a. *Rubber bands.* It is important that you buy *long thin* rubber bands. Buy those $3\frac{1}{2}$ inches long and $\frac{1}{16}$ inch or less in diameter.

b. *Faucet connector.* Buy this for 5 cents at a ten-cent store.

c. *Large balloons.* Buy at least two at 5 cents each.

d. *Medium balloons.* Buy at least two at two for 5 cents.

e. *Small balloons.* Buy five at 1 cent each.

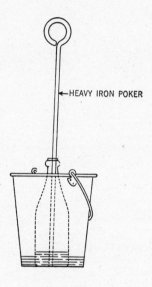

←HEAVY IRON POKER

12. Another Way to Cut the Bottom From a Bottle

Fill the bottle with water to the point at which you wish it to break.

Stand it in a pail of water of the same depth.

Heat one end of a thick iron poker red hot *for a length of 8 inches* or more.

Place it in the water in the bottle and the bottom will crack off.

Smooth the rough edges with a file.

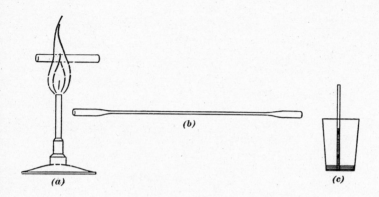

13. A Capillary Tube

a. Cut a piece of No. 2 glass tubing 5 inches long, and heat it in a Bunsen flame until it is quite soft.

b. Remove it from the flame and stretch it two feet or more. Break the narrow part into capillary tubes of about one foot length.

c. Place one end of one in a tablespoonful of ink in a tumbler. The ink will rise to a surprising height in the capillary tube.

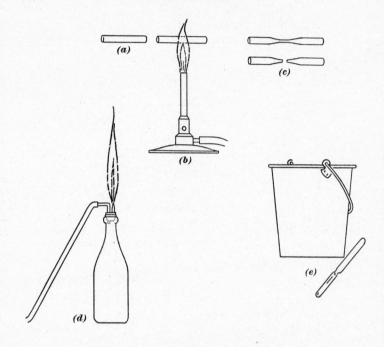

14. A Sound-Wave Detector

a. Cut a piece of No. 2 glass tubing 5 inches long, and smooth its ends. Let it cool.

b. Turn it in a Bunsen flame above the green cone until it is soft.

c. Remove it from the flame, stretch it about two inches, and after it has cooled break the stretched part. You then have two pointed nozzles.

d. Arrange the equipment, turn on the gas and get a flame, 10 inches or more high, which is just about to flare. Use a nozzle with a *rough uneven mouth*. This is important.

e. Strike a tin pail with the blade of a knife to make a sharp sound and the tall flame will "duck" when the sound wave passes through it.

EXPLANATIONS

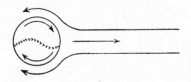

BASEBALL CURVES AND THE LIKE

1—Bernoulli's Principle is: A rapid stream of gas or liquid is surrounded by a low-pressure area and the more rapid the stream the lower is the pressure.

The ball above is moving through air *to the right*. We can, however, think of the ball as stationary with air streams moving around it *to the left*.

If the ball is revolving as shown, its upper surface retards the top air stream and its lower surface accelerates the bottom air stream.

The faster air stream and lower pressure are below, by Bernoulli's Principle. Hence the atmosphere forces the ball downward in a "drop."

Revolving tennis and golf balls curve, for the same reason.

2—A revolving ball always curves in the direction in which its front is revolving. That is, "it follows its front" in curving, for the reason given in 1.

The ping-pong ball rolls along the *right* inner side of the mailing tube when you move the tube rapidly from *right* to left, hence its front is revolving toward the *right* when it leaves the tube. The ball then "follows its front" and curves to the *right*.

The ball rolls along the *left* inner side of the tube when you move the tube rapidly from *left* to right and its front is revolving toward the *left* when it leaves the tube. The ball then "follows its front" and curves to the *left*.

3—The ball, when shot forward, is started revolving by the drag of the electric tape. It "follows its front" in each case and curves in the direction its front is revolving.

4—Similar to 1, 2, and 3.

5—The tube "follows its front" and curves upward, but it is rotating so rapidly that it continues to "follow its front"; and it makes one complete loop, 360°, and sometimes two, 720°, before it reaches the ground.

6—The ping-pong ball is surrounded by rapidly moving air, hence it is surrounded by a low-pressure area, by Bernoulli's Principle. The ball remains in the air stream because if it moves to the edge, the greater atmospheric pressure on its outer side shoves it back into the stream against the lower pressure exerted against its inner side by the rapid air stream.
The ball is *supported* by the upward force of the air stream.

7—Similar to 6.

8—Similar to 6.

9—The ball and balloons, by their inertia, tend to remain where they are when the vertical air stream moves horizontally. When they reach the rear edge of the stream, however, they are shoved forward into the air stream by the atmospheric pressure on their outer side, as explained in 6.

10—*a.* The rapid air stream produces an area of low pressure above the paper and the greater atmospheric pressure below the paper lifts it into the air stream.

  b. The air stream is spread upward, sidewise, and downward by the screen, and produces an area of low pressure at and beyond the edges of the screen.
  The atmosphere on the candle side of the screen moves air toward this low-pressure area and thereby blows the candle flames *toward* the screen.

  c. The air stream divides and produces a low-pressure area between each half-stream and the pail. Each half-stream is held against the pail by the atmosphere. They pass around the pail, unite on the far side, and blow out the flame.

11—The water stream divides and produces a low-pressure area between each half-stream and the pail. The half-streams are held against the pail by the atmosphere. They unite on the far side where they meet head on.

12—The water stream produces a low-pressure area between itself and the side of the balloon it touches. The atmosphere behind the balloon and stream holds them together. You feel a fairly strong pull because the balloon is shoved *into* the stream and part of the water falls on its upper side. Your upward pull must balance the downward force of this upper water and also the weight of the water which clings to the under side of the balloon.

13—There is an upward flow of water as well as a downward flow, because the water which enters the tumbler must come out again; and it is the upward flow which lifts the egg.

It is the Bernoulli Effect of the upward and downward flows, however, which keeps the egg centered in the middle of the flows. If the egg starts to move out of the flows the greater velocity and lower pressure are on its inner side, and the greater pressure on its outer side shoves it back into the flows.

14—Similar to 1, 2, and 3.

15—Similar to 1, 2, and 3.

16—Similar to 1, 2, and 3.

CENTRIFUGAL FORCE

17—If a body is moving in a circle, the force with which its weight pulls away from the center of the circle is called the *centrifugal force* of the weight. The greater the weight and the greater its speed the greater is its centrifugal force.

The equal and opposite force which must be exerted toward the center to keep the weight in its circular path is called the *centripetal force.*

a. The centrifugal force produced by the weight of the spikes moving in a circle tends to move these weights as far as possible away from the center of the circle. This condition is fulfilled when the circle is horizontal.

b. The centrifugal force produced by the weight of the single spike moving in a circle tends to move this weight as far as possible away from the center of the circle. It is this centrifugal force which lifts the spike from a vertical to a horizontal position.

18—In each case the centrifugal force lifts the body from a vertical to a horizontal position, because in this horizontal position the greatest amount of the weight of the body is farthest from the center or axis of revolution and the total centrifugal force is greatest. A body tends to revolve about its shortest axis when its center of gravity is below its point of support.

19—a. The tall coffee can wobbles because it is trying to lie on its side and revolve about its shortest axis which is perpendicular to the sides of the can at a point slightly nearer the bottom than the top, due to the weight of the can bottom. In this position the greatest amount of its weight is as far as it can get from the axis of revolution.

b. The squat can does not wobble because it revolves about its shortest axis and as much as possible of its weight is as far as it can get from this axis.

20—The centrifugal force produced by any weight revolving in a circle pulls that weight as far as possible away from the center of the circle.

   a. The centrifugal force of the water moving in a circle moves the water away from the center, up the inside and over the top.

   b. The centrifugal force of the water moving in a circle moves the water as far as possible from the center or axis of revolution—that is, to the equator of the bowl.

21—Similar to 20.

22—*a.* The weight exerts *centrifugal force* and you must exert an equal and opposite *centripetal force* to keep it in a circular path.

   b. Similar to *a.*

23—*a.* The centrifugal force of the water and sand moves them to the sides of the bottle.

   b. When you place the bottle on the table the water surface is high at the sides and low at the center. As the water moves more slowly in its circular motion its centrifugal force decreases. Also as the water surface sinks at the sides and rises at the center, there is a current of water down the sides, across the bottom toward the center and up the center. It is this current of water which moves the heavier sand to the middle of the bottom.

Other Mechanical Principles

24—The "center of percussion" is the scientific name for the "best spot" on a bat. If this center of percussion strikes the ball, the bat "moves as a whole" and there is no vibration.

If a point other than the center of percussion strikes the ball, the bat bends forward with its center of percussion ahead of its ends; the next instant the bat bends backward with its center of percussion behind its ends. This to-and-fro bending takes place very rapidly and it is this vibration which stings your hands.

25—You swing the ball in an arc of a circle, with your foot or feet as the center and your leg, body, and arm the radius. The greater the speed you give the ball in this circular arc the greater the speed it has when it leaves your hand.

26—It has been learned in thousands of tests that any body falling vertically downward gains velocity at the rate of 32.16 feet a second each second it falls, if the air resistance is small.

Similarly, it has been learned that any body thrown vertically upward loses velocity at the rate of 32.16 feet a second each second it rises, if the air resistance is small. The air resistance is small on compact smooth bodies at low speeds. For convenience we will use 32 instead of 32.16.

A ball thrown vertically upward loses velocity as it rises, and gains the same velocity in the opposite direction as it falls. It rises half the time and falls half the time.

If the ball was in the air for 5 seconds, it rose for 2½ seconds and since it lost velocity at the rate of 32 feet a second each second it rose, it left your hand with a velocity of *32 × 2½ = 80* feet a second.

27—*Newton's Second Law of Motion is:*
Change of momentum is in the direction of the impressed force and proportional to it and to the time during which it acts. The *momentum* of a body is the quantity of motion possessed by the body and it is defined as the product of the mass and velocity of the body.

A mass weighing 10 lbs. and moving with a velocity of 20 feet a second has a momentum of *10 × 20 = 200.*

a. The mass of one clothes-pin is equal to that of the other. The force the stretched rubber band exerts on one pin is equal to the force it exerts on the other, but in the opposite direction. The time the stretched band acts on one pin is equal to the time it acts on the other. By Newton's Second Law of Motion, equal forces acting in opposite directions on equal masses for equal times produce equal velocities in opposite directions. The pins will meet at the middle point.

b. Here again the forces are equal and opposite and the times are equal, hence the momenta produced will be equal and opposite. But the two pins have twice the mass of the single pin, hence the velocity given to the two pins will be half that given to the single pin and the pins will meet as shown.

28—a. Here the forces are equal and in opposite directions, the times are equal and the masses are equal. Hence by Newton's Second Law of Motion the momenta and velocities produced will be equal and in opposite directions.

b. Here the forces are equal and in opposite directions and the times are equal but the mass on one side is twice that on the other. By Newton's Second Law of Motion the momenta produced will be equal and in opposite directions and the velocities produced will be in opposite directions, but the velocity of the heavy mass will be only one-half that of the lighter mass.

c. In *a* the force of the spring acts on two pins, one on each side. Here the force of the spring acts on only one pin for the same time, hence it gives the pin twice the velocity it gave each pin in *a*.

29—a. A falling body gains velocity at the rate of 32 feet a second each second it falls.

Its velocity at the start is 0 feet per second.
Its velocity at the end of 1 second is 32 feet a second.
Its velocity at the end of 2 seconds is 64 feet a second.
Its velocity at the end of 3 seconds is 96 feet a second.
Its velocity at the end of 4 seconds is 128 feet a second.

Its *average* velocity *during* the first second is:

$$\frac{\text{Velocity at start} + \text{velocity at end}}{2} = \frac{0 + 32}{2} = 16 \text{ feet a second.}$$

Space traveled in the first second $= 16 \times 1 = 16$ feet.

Its *average* velocity *during* the first two seconds is:

$$\frac{\text{Velocity at start} + \text{velocity at end}}{2} = \frac{0 + 64}{2} = 32 \text{ feet a second.}$$

Space traveled in the first two seconds $= 32 \times 2 = 64$ feet.

b. Let us say that the heavy body has twice the mass of the light body. Then the force of attraction of the earth on the heavy body will be twice that on the light body.

The *force acting* in one case is *twice* that acting in the other but the *mass set in motion* is also twice as great, hence the *velocities produced* in *equal times* are *equal*. The bodies reach the ground with equal velocities in equal times no matter what their masses may be. See Newton's Second Law of Motion, Experiences 27 and 28.

30—Here the vertical height of one slide is equal to that of the other. If there were no friction between the slide and the marble, then according to mathematical theory, the velocity at the bottom of one slide would be exactly equal to that at the bottom of the other, no matter what may be the mass of the marbles, the length of the slides, or the shape of the slides.

Friction is anything which opposes motion and there is friction in each case. Each slide opposes the motion of its marble slightly because the marble sinks into the plane slightly and the friction is proportional to the pressure the marble exerts perpendicular to the plane. It decreases, however, as the velocity increases because at high velocity the marble sinks into the plane less than at low velocity.

The marble on the curved plane meets less friction than the one on the straight plane, because during the first part of

the slide its path is steeper and it exerts less pressure
perpendicular to the plane. Also during the last part of the
slide its velocity is greater and it sinks less into the plane.

The friction is less and therefore the velocity is greater
on the curved than on the straight plane.

31—A force has the same effect whether it acts alone or with
other forces.

The force of gravity pulls vertically downward on the coin
which falls vertically downward. It also pulls vertically
downward on the coin which moves sidewise due to the
horizontal blow. It has the same effect on each coin and
pulls both downward equal distances in equal times.

32—If you can jump *upward* at a velocity of say 16 feet a second,
you will rise $\frac{16}{32}$ or $\frac{1}{2}$ second because you will lose upward
velocity at the rate of 32 feet a second each second you rise.
You will also fall for $\frac{1}{2}$ second, hence you will be in the air
$\frac{1}{2} + \frac{1}{2}$ or 1 second.

If your horizontal velocity is 25 feet a second, your broad
jump will be 25 feet.

33—The force exerted by each hand can be resolved into a
horizontal component and a vertical component. The horizontal components are equal and opposite and balance one
another. The vertical components support the weight. Each
hand uses up nearly all of its force in pulling against the
other hand.

34—The short bent part prevents the straw from sliding out of
the bottle.

35—The lever arm of each weight is the horizontal distance from
the fulcrum to the point at which the weight is hung. The
law of the lever is: Any lever balances when the product of
the weight and its lever arm on one side of the fulcrum is
equal to the similar product on the other side of the fulcrum.

36—The pulleys fastened together constitute a revolving lever
with the axle as the fulcrum. The lever law holds for
revolving levers.

37—*Newton's Third Law of Motion states:* To every action there
is an equal and opposite reaction. The baseball must be given
a slight sidewise motion to make it miss the pencil on the
forward swing. This "action" will produce an equal and
opposite "reaction" which will make the baseball miss the
pencil by an equal distance on the opposite side during the
backward swing.

38—The swinging pendulum gives the second pendulum a slight push, through the cross bar, each time it swings and in doing so gives up some of its energy. These pushes set the second pendulum swinging because each comes at exactly the right time and in the right direction. This continues until the first pendulum comes to rest because it has given all of its energy to the other pendulum. The second pendulum is now in full swing and it begins to set the first pendulum swinging again, and so on.

Note. This works best when the pendulums are of exactly the same length and hence have exactly equal times of swing, or periods.

Gases

39—The baseball shoves air aside during each swing and thereby loses the energy it gives to the air. As a result, each swing is a little shorter than the preceding swing.

40—*c.* The cover and the paper must each shove air aside to reach the floor. The cover, due to its greater weight, does this more quickly than the paper.

d. The cover here shoves the air aside for the paper and they reach the floor together.

41—The balloon rubber is held so firmly against the cup by air pressure that it makes an excellent grip.

42—The water keeps on moving when the bottle stops. It moves down in the bottle along the side farthest from the experimenter, across the bottom and up along the near side. It gives up its energy in compressing the air at the top of the bottle and this compressed air in turn gives up this energy in lifting the cork. The "pop" you hear when the cork comes out is caused by the sudden expansion of the compressed air.

43—The acid dissolves the zinc and liberates hydrogen. The chemical equation is:

Zinc + hydrochloric acid = zinc chloride + hydrogen
$Zn \ + 2\,HCl$ $= ZnCl_2$ $+ H_2$

Hydrogen weighs only about one fourteenth as much as air volume for volume. The balloon rises when the upward force acting on it is greater than the downward force. The upward force is equal to the weight of the air displaced by the balloon. The downward force is equal to the weight of the balloon rubber and cord, plus the weight of the hydrogen in the balloon. See the Law of Archimedes for gases in 45.

44—The household lye is sodium hydroxide. It dissolves the aluminum and liberates hydrogen. The chemical equation is:

Alumium + Sodium hydrate + water
$2\,Al$ $+ 2\,NaOH$ $+ 2\,H_2O$
= Sodium aluminate + hydrogen
$= 2\,NaAlO_2$ $+ 3\,H_2$

The balloon rises for the reason given in 43.

45—a. The hot water warms the carbon-tetrachloride liquid and turns it into a gas quickly.

b. Carbon-tetrachloride is CCl_4. The atomic weight of carbon is 12 and that of chlorine is 35.5, hence the molecular weight of CCl_4 is $12 + (4 \times 35.5) = 12 + 142 = 154$.

Air is not a compound but if it were its molecular weight would be 28.8, hence carbon-tetrachloride *gas* is $\frac{154}{28.8} = 5.3$ times as heavy as air, volume for volume.

The Law of Archimedes for gases is: Any body placed in a gas is buoyed up by a force equal to the weight of the gas it displaces. The air bubble floats when the weight of the CCl_4 gas it displaces is equal to its own weight.

46—The paper bags are filled with air and one of them rises because it is buoyed up by a force equal to the weight of the CCl_4 gas it displaces.

47—The CCl_4 gas does not support combustion and it pours because it is 5.3 times as heavy as air volume for volume.

48—The bag filled with CCl_4 gas sinks because CCl_4 gas is 5.3 times as heavy as air volume for volume. See Experience 45.

49—The baking soda and vinegar combine and liberate carbon-dioxide gas. The chemical equation is
Baking soda + vinegar = sodium acetate + carbon-dioxide + water
$NaHCO_3$ $+ CH_3COOH = CH_3COONa$ $+ CO_2$ $+ H_2O$

The atomic weight of carbon is 12, and of oxygen 16, hence molecular weight of carbon-dioxide gas is $12 + 2 \times 16 = 44$, and carbon-dioxide gas is $\frac{44}{28.8} = 1.5$ times as heavy as air volume for volume.

Carbon-dioxide gas does not support combustion and it pours because it is heavier than air, volume for volume.

50—The air in each balloon is under pressure, hence it is compressed and it weighs more than an equal volume of outside air.

Each balloon is buoyed up by a force equal to the weight of the outside air it displaces.

The weight hanging on each bent pin then is: The weight of the balloon and cord, plus the weight of the air compressed in the balloon, minus the weight of the outside air displaced by the balloon.

When one balloon is emptied, the weight of the small volume of air left in it is supported by the buoyant force of the air it displaces. Hence, the only weight on the bent pin is that of the balloon and cord, and this side is raised by the weight of the air in the other balloon plus the weight of this balloon and its cord minus the weight of the air displaced.

Liquids

51—*The Law of Archimedes* for liquids is: A body placed in a liquid is buoyed up by a force equal to the weight of the liquid it displaces.

A cubic foot of fresh water weighs about 62.3 lbs., hence, by the Law of Archimedes, for each cubic foot you displace the water buoys you up with a force of 62.3 lbs.

If your volume is 2 cubic feet, the maximum buoyant force on your body in fresh water is $62.3 \times 2 = 124.6$ lbs.

Conversely, if you weigh 190 lbs. in air, but only 3 lbs. when completely submerged in fresh water, the buoyant force of the water on you is $190-3=187$ lbs. and your volume is $\frac{187}{62.3} = 3$ cubic feet.

52—*d.* Water is nearly incompressible but air is easily compressed. The pressure you exert on the water with the palm of your right hand is transmitted by the water to the air in the bottle and compresses it. This decreases the volume of water displaced by the air and, by the Law of Archimedes, decreases the buoyant force on the bottle and air. The bottle and air then sink by gravity.

When you decrease the pressure on the water, the air in the bottle expands and increases the volume of water displaced. This increases the buoyant force of the water on the bottle and air until it is great enough to lift them against the force of gravity.

53—*b.* The buoy sinks until the volume of water it displaces has a weight, and buoyant force, equal to its own weight.

c. It does not sink so far in salt water as in fresh, because salt water is heavier volume for volume than fresh water.

d. It sinks to the bottom in kerosene because it cannot displace a weight of kerosene equal to its own weight, since kerosene is only $\frac{8}{10}$ as heavy as fresh water, volume for volume.

54—d. The submarine sinks until it displaces a weight of the combined fresh and salt water equal to its own weight.

55—b. The can is filled with water until the weight is exactly 1 lb.

c. It sinks in water until the volume of water it displaces has a weight, and buoyant force, of exactly 1 lb. It then floats and exerts no downward pull on the scale, that is, it appears to have no weight at all.

56—See the Law of Archimedes, Experience 51. The can and the water in it weigh exactly 1 lb., and they sink until they displace a volume of water which has a weight, and buoyant force, of exactly 1 lb.

57—See the Law of Archimedes, Experience 51. The rock displaces its own volume of water and since the buoyant force of this displaced water is 12 ounces, the weight of the displaced water must be 12 ounces.

58—This proves that the weight of the displaced water is 12 ounces.

59—*Pascal's Law for Liquids is:* Pressure exerted on a confined liquid is transmitted *equally* and *undiminished* in all directions by the liquid, and is exerted at right angles to the surface of the container.

If the pressure exerted on the stopper by the blow of the hammer is say, 50 lbs. per sq. in., this is the outward pressure on *each* sq. in. of the inside of the bottle. If the total area of the bottle is say, 20 sq. in., the total bursting force is $20 \times 50 = 1,000$ lbs.

60—The surface of a liquid acts like a fairly strong film. The surface of cold water is quite strong. The surface of hot soapy water is about one-half as strong, and those of kerosene and carbon tetrachloride are respectively about one-third and one-fourth as strong as the surface of pure cold water.

The razor blades float on the strong surfaces and break through the weak surfaces.

61—Paper should float on any liquid because it is lighter volume for volume than any liquid.

It sinks in a liquid when the liquid runs up into its pores and *pulls it down.*

Its pores are very small and the surface of the liquid *must bend into a very small pointed angle* in order to enter them.

The paper sinks slowly in cold water because the surface of cold water is strong and does not bend easily. It sinks rapidly in kerosene and carbon tetrachloride because their surfaces are weak and bend easily.

Note: Every good cleansing liquid has a weak surface which bends readily into pores and into the narrow space between dirt and the dirty surface to be cleaned.

62—Lycopodium powder does not absorb water readily. It forms a film on your thumb and fingers which prevents the water from reaching them.

63—*a.* The surface of any liquid tends to contract to the smallest possible area. This contracting force or tension is called the *surface tension* of the liquid.

A sphere is the volume which has the smallest possible area of surface for a given volume. The lycopodium powder forms an outer layer on each drop which prevents the water from touching the saucer. The surface tension of the water then pulls the drop into a perfect sphere.

If the water does touch the saucer the sphere is flattened at once, because the *adhesion* between the saucer and water is greater than the *cohesion* of the water.

b. The surface tension of the water pulls small volumes of water into perfect spheres.

64—*a.* The water penetrates into the pores of the paper and rises in the pores because the *adhesion* between the paper molecules, just above the water surface, and the water molecules in the surface, is greater than the *cohesion* between the water molecules. It stops rising when the cohesion plus the weight of the water column raised equals the adhesion. This is called capillarity.

b. Similar to *a.*

c. The water rises in the cloth as in *b,* and runs down into the outer half. The water in the cloth then becomes in effect a siphon.

65—*a.* The ink rises in the sugar for the reason given in 64—a.

c. The salt forms crystals around the edge of the surface, then salt water rises in these crystals by capillarity and forms more crystals just above. This continues and salt crystals move up the inside of the tumbler to the top and frequently down the outside.

66—Water enters the dry wood cells in the bend of a match and *swells* the cells. This swelling tends to straighten the match and makes its ends move farther apart. The ends of the five matches meet and make a five-pointed star.

67—Water enters the paper cells in each bend it touches, and swells them. This swelling straightens the bends and makes the serpent stretch.

Heat

68—Dry ice is solid carbon-dioxide, CO_2. It is at a temperature of minus 110° F. It is called dry because it changes directly from a solid to a gas without going through the liquid state. That is, it "sublimes".

A piece of water ice also sublimes if it is left outdoors in winter when the temperature is below 32° F. That is, it evaporates directly from a solid to a gas without going through the liquid state.

a. Heat from the water changes the carbon-dioxide solid into carbon-dioxide gas, which is invisible. The CO_2 gas is so very cold that it condenses water vapor into a visible cloud, that is, into millions of minute drops of water.

b. The cloud is mixed with CO_2 gas which is heavier than air. See Experience 49. A bubble filled with air floats when it displaces a weight of this mixture equal to its own weight. *The Law of Archimedes for gases is:* Any body placed in a gas is buoyed up by a force equal to the weight of gas it displaces.

c. Carbon-dioxide gas does not support combustion.

d. Carbon-dioxide gas pours because it is heavier than air, volume for volume. Also cold air is heavier than warm air, volume for volume.

69—*a.* The part of the knife that touches the dry ice at − 110° F. contracts rapidly as it cools. It also expands rapidly when it no longer touches the dry ice. This contraction and expansion sets up irregular vibrations which cause the groaning sounds.

b. The rubber loses some of its elasticity when it is cooled.

c. Heat from the thermometer bulb moves through air and CO_2 gas slowly because gases are poor conductors of heat.

d. Kerosene is a slightly better conductor of heat than is a gas.

70—Water turns to steam when it boils, the steam leaves the kettle, and that part of it which is cooled by the cold water turns back to water.

Since the solid impurities in the water do not turn to a gas they remain in the kettle.

71—The expansive force of the steam lifts the saucer and the balloon.

72—The gasoline liquid turns to a gas very rapidly and the gas mixes with the air in the can. The mixture burns very rapidly and produces a great deal of heat which expands the mixture very rapidly. This rapid expansion is the explosion which lifts the can cover.

73—*a*. The steam fills the bottle and drives out the air.

b. The stopper keeps air out of the bottle.

c. The cold water condenses much of the steam in the bottle. There is then less steam above the water and therefore less pressure on the water. Under this lowered pressure the water boils and produces more steam. The cold water condenses this steam and lowers the pressure still more. The water boils at a lower temperature at this lower pressure, and so on.

74—The writer is not sure of the explanation of this phenomenon. Apparently the salt prevents the linen from being burned completely but permits it to be turned into a thread of carbon. Each small weight seems to be supported by a thread composed of carbon and fused salt.

75—Metals expand when heated and contract when cooled.

76—The tumbler is heated by the hot water and it in turn warms the cold air which fills it after the hot water is emptied out.

The tumbler is raised slightly above the glass plate by the heat expansion of the cold air and it is then pulled by gravity down the slide. Its path is lubricated by the hot water which drips down its inner side.

77—Air expands when heated and hence cold air is heavier than hot air, volume for volume. The cold heavy air is pulled down the cold-air chimney by gravity and it *lifts* the hot light air up through the hot-air chimney.

78—*a*. Part of the energy you expend in rubbing the tack on the floor or carpet is turned into heat and this heat warms the tack and also the floor or carpet.

b. Each rosin particle burns rapidly with a long flame and this long flame looks like lightning.

79—A *rough* surface radiates and absorbs heat more quickly than a *smooth* surface. The *color* of the surface influences the result only slightly.

80—*First surprise.* The solution feels cold, because when the salt is dissolved in water it is turned into a liquid and it absorbs from the water some of the heat required to melt it.

Second surprise. The solution has a larger volume than the water, because the water plus the salt occupies more space than the water alone.

Ammonium chloride crystallizes out of a concentrated solution very rapidly and the small crystals sink because they are heavier volume for volume than the concentrated solution. The falling crystals look like falling snow-flakes, which are water crystals.

81—Directions.

82—All liquids are poor conductors of heat.

83—*a.* The temperature at which ice melts is by definition 32° F.

b. Salt makes ice melt more rapidly than it would if there were no salt present and the heat required to melt the ice comes partly from the surroundings and partly from the mixture itself. When the mixture loses heat it cools below the temperature of the melting ice.

c. Water evaporating from the cloth takes heat from the surroundings and from the bulb to which it is attached and it thereby cools the thermometer. The drier the air the more rapid is the evaporation and the greater the cooling, and vice versa.

84—The standards for household refrigerators are:
45° F. or less in the milk space, the cold space;
50° F. or less in the food space;
below 32° F. in the ice-cube space.

WATER PRESSURE

A cubic foot of water weighs 62.3 lbs. at ordinary temperatures. If then we have a tank $1' \times 1' \times 1'$ and fill it with water the pressure on the 1 square-foot base is 62.3 lbs.

One square foot is $12'' \times 12''$ or 144 sq. in., hence the pressure on each *square inch* of the base is $\frac{62.3}{144} = .43$ lb., a little less than ½ lb.

We will show in "balancing water columns," Experience 96, that the pressure exerted by a liquid on a given surface depends not at all on the *volume* of the liquid, but only on the *density* of the liquid and its *height* above the surface.

The pressure anywhere 1 foot under water is .43 lb. per sq. in.; two feet under water the pressure is .43 × 2 = .86 lb. per sq. in.; at five feet under water, the pressure is .43 × 5 or 2.15 lbs. per sq. in., and so on.

85—The long water column in the tank and long rubber tube exerts pressure on the air in the lower bottle, compresses it, and drives it up through the short rubber tube into the top of the upper bottle.

Here the pressure of the compressed air lifts the shorter column of water measured from the water surface in the upper bottle to the top of the water jet.

It is not perpetual motion because as soon as the lower bottle and short rubber tube are filled with water, the jet will no longer rise above the water level in the tank.

86—The pressure of the water in the tank and tubes produces the fountain.

87—The pressure of the water in the tank and tubes compresses the air in the bottle after the water level in the bottle reaches the lower end of the lower union. The pressure of the compressed air then lifts the water and produces the fountain.

88—The pressure of the water at each nozzle is equal to that of a column of water measured from the middle of the outlet of the nozzle to the water surface in the bottomless bottle. Hence the pressure at the lower nozzle is greater than that at the upper.

89—Method.

90—*Pascal's Law states:* Pressure on a confined liquid is transmitted by the liquid equally and undiminished in all directions, and is exerted at right angles to each point on the inside surface of the container.

   a. The pressure at each hole at the equator is at right angles to the surface and is equal to that at every other hole.

   b. The pressure at each hole above the equator is at right angles to the surface and is equal to that at the equator *minus* the pressure of the column of water measured from the level of the equator to that of the hole.

91—This is another illustration of Pascal's Law.

92—The top surface of the hot-water bag is about 10 inches long and 7 inches wide, and it has an area of *10 × 7 = 70* sq. in. If the water column in the tank and tubes exerts a pressure of say 2 lbs. per sq. in. on the water at the mouth of the bag, this pressure, by Pascal's Law, is transmitted equally and undiminished by the water; and the pressure on the inside surface of the bag is 2 lbs. per sq. in.

The total lift on the upper surface is then *70 × 2 = 140* lbs. This force will lift many pints of water.

93—If the pressure of the water from the faucet is say 20 lbs. per sq. in. at the mouth of the bag, the pressure on each sq. in. of the inside surface of the bag is 20 lbs. by Pascal's Law.

If the area of the top of the bag is 70 sq. in. as in Experience 92, the total life is *70 × 20 = 1,400* lbs. It will lift you and many others.

94—The force of the water drives the wheel.

95—*Newton's Third Law of Motion states:* To every action there is an equal and opposite reaction.

The water leaves an elbow in one direction with a certain force. This is the "action" and, by Newton's Third Law, it exerts an equal force in the opposite direction on the elbow. It is this latter force, the "reaction," which turns the turbine.

96—*The Hydrostatic Paradox is:* The pressure exerted by a stationary column of liquid is entirely independent of the *volume* of liquid in the column. It depends only on the height and density of the liquid.

The *density* of a liquid is its weight per unit volume, for example, its weight per cubic inch, cubic foot, or cubic centimeter.

These experiences illustrate the Hydrostatic Paradox.

97—The water poured into the right-hand tumbler exerts pressure upward on the air in the large glass tube. This pressure is transmitted equally and undiminished by the air and exerted on the water in the U-tube.

The difference in height of the columns of water in the U-tube is exactly equal to the column of water measured from the water surface in the large glass tube to that in the tumbler.

98—The *momentum* of any body is defined as its quantity of motion. It is equal to the product of its weight and velocity.

a. The water in the horizontal tube has momentum because it has weight and velocity.

b. When you pinch the union you destroy the horizontal velocity but you do not destroy the momentum. It is used up in giving the small weight of water in the vertical tube a greater vertical velocity which carries it above the level of the water in the bottomless bottle.

99—a. c. By the hydrostatic paradox, the pressure of a *stationary* column of water at a given point is independent of the volume of water in the column and depends only on the height of the water above the given point.

b. d. The hydrostatic paradox does not apply when the water is in motion.

Here the *head* or pressure which is producing the motion is that of the column measured vertically from the outlet to the water level in the bottomless bottle.

Part of this pressure is producing motion and the remainder is producing static pressure in the vertical tube. The greater the velocity produced the less is the static pressure.

e. The head here is more than doubled and this increases the velocity to such an extent that the static pressure at a point near the bottle is less than zero or negative. Negative pressure is called "suction."

ATMOSPHERIC PRESSURE

The atmosphere of the earth is attracted by the earth and hence it has weight. It exerts a pressure of 14.7 pounds, nearly 15 pounds, on each square inch of everything on the earth's surface at sea level. It exerts this pressure equally in all directions upward, downward, and sidewise, at a given level.

A pressure of 14.7 lbs. per sq. in. is equal to that of a column of water 34 feet deep. This means that if the atmosphere of the earth were removed and replaced by an ocean of water 34 feet deep, the pressure 34 feet under water would be the same as that exerted by the atmosphere, namely 14.7 lbs. per sq. in.

The atmosphere can support a column of water 34 feet high at sea level if there is a vacuum, or zero pressure, at the top of the column.

For convenience we will call the pressure of the atmosphere at sea level 15 lbs. per sq. in. instead of 14.7.

100—b. The steam drives the air out of the milk bottle.

c. When the steam cools and condenses to water it leaves nearly a vacuum in the bottle. The atmosphere pressing down on the water surface in the pail can lift water 34 feet high and it lifts the water 6 or 8 feet up into the bottle easily.

101—The steam drives nearly all the air out of the milk bottle and leaves a fairly high vacuum when it condenses to water.

The air in the soda bottle then expands into the low-pressure area in the milk bottle and this decreases the air pressure in the soda bottle. The atmospheric pressure on

the water surface in the pail then lifts water up the tube
into the soda bottle and produces the fountain.

102—Similar to 101.

103—Before you start these experiences, the milk bottle is open
to the air. It is full of air and this air exerts a pressure
outward equal to the pressure the atmosphere exerts inward,
namely, 15 lbs. per sq. in.

The burning paper you drop into the milk bottle produces
heat which expands the air in the bottle to about 3 times
its volume and about two-thirds of the air leaves the bottle.
When the one-third quart of air left in the bottle cools to
room temperature it exerts only one-third the pressure the
air in the full bottle did at first or $\frac{1}{3} \times 15 = 5$ lbs. per sq.
in. The atmosphere outside exerts a pressure of 15 lbs.
per sq. in., and it moves the water toward the low-pressure
space in the milk bottle.

104—This demonstrates that the pressure of the atmosphere is
equal in all directions at a given point.

105—*c.* The pressure of the atmosphere on the water surface in the
pail and on the top side of the rubber sheet is equal to that
of a column of water 34 feet high.

If the height from the water surface in the pail to the under
side of the rubber sheet is, say 6 feet, the atmospheric
pressure on the water surface in the pail is supporting a
column of water 6 feet high and its upward pressure on the
under side of the rubber sheet is equal to that of a column
of water only $34 - 6$ or 28 feet high.

The difference between the pressures on the two sides of
the rubber sheet is equal to that of a column of water
$34-28 = 6$ feet high.

Suction. In this experience the 6-foot column of water
under the rubber sheet *appears to draw down* the sheet.
This *apparent drawing* is called suction. It is a convenient
name and we will use it. But you must remember that in
every case what appears to be suction is really the difference
in pressure at two points.

106—When you suck air out of the bottle you decrease the air
in the bottle and thereby decrease the pressure the remaining
air exerts on the surface of the balloon in the bottle. The
atmosphere pressing on the surface of the balloon outside
the bottle then forces the part of the balloon under the
bottle up into the bottle.

107—*a.* When you suck air out of the tank you decrease the pressure the air exerts on the part of your arm under the

tank. The pressure of the atmosphere on the remainder of your arm and body then forces that part up into the tank.

b. Similar to *a.*

108—Similar to 105, 106, and 107.

109—When you suck air out of the bottle you decrease the pressure the air in the bottle exerts on the outside of the balloon. The atmosphere outside then forces air into the balloon through the coupling and expands the balloon.

When you let air flow into the bottle again, the pressure on the outer side of the balloon becomes equal to that of the atmosphere outside. The balloon rubber contracts and drives out air until it arrives at its first condition.

110—*b.* The raised diaphragm forces air out of the bottle because the neck is open.

c. The lowered diaphragm expands the air in the bottle because the neck is closed.

The expansion decreases the air pressure in the bottle and the atmosphere forces outside air into the balloon.

111—The water inside sinks slowly when you raise the bottomless bottle. It thereby gives the air in the bottle more room and decreases its pressure. The atmosphere outside then forces air and smoke through the smoke producer into the bottle.

112—*a.* When you suck water through the tube, what you really do is this: You increase the volume of your mouth cavity and thereby decrease the pressure of the air in your mouth and in the top of the tube. The atmosphere pressing down on the water in the bottle then lifts water up through the tube into your mouth.

b. You cannot suck water from the bottle because the atmosphere cannot exert pressure on the water in the bottle.

113—*a.* When you invert the upper bottle into the bottomless bottle, air enters the upper bottle and water leaves it until the water level in the bottomless bottle is slightly above the mouth of the upper bottle. Then the air inflow is stopped by the water in the bottomless bottle, and the water outflow is stopped by the atmospheric pressure on the water surface in the bottomless bottle.

b. When the water level drops below the mouth of the upper bottle, air enters the upper bottle and increases the air pressure above the water. This permits water to flow out until the water level is again slightly above the mouth of the upper bottle.

114—Similar to 113.

115—*b*. The water is supported by the strength of the water surface at the lower end of the small hole in the lower stopper and by the upward pressure of the atmosphere on this surface.

The water flows out when the upper stopper is removed because the upward atmospheric pressure on its lower surface is balanced by an equal downward atmospheric pressure on its upper surface and the lower water surface is not strong enough to support the water column.

116—The atmosphere extends many miles above the earth but its height above the top floor of any building is less than it is above the basement. Hence its pressure at the top floor is less than it is in the basement.

117—When you suck out air you decrease the air pressure above the water and the atmospheric pressure on the water surface in the vessel lifts the water columns.

The water columns are of the same height because:

1. By Pascal's Law pressure exerted by the atmosphere on the water surface is transmitted equally and undiminished by the water to the bottom of the water columns.

2. By the hydrostatic paradox, the water columns exert equal downward pressures when their heights are equal, no matter what their volume may be. See Experience 96.

118—When you suck air out of the bottle you give the air remaining in the bottle more room and thereby decrease the air pressure in the bottle. The atmosphere outside pressing down on the water surface in the tumbler or pail then lifts water up into the bottle.

119—When you blow air into the bottle you increase the air pressure in the bottle and this air pressure lifts water up into the large glass tube.

SIPHONS

120—*d*. Three operations follow one another, as follows:

1. The water runs out of the bottle by gravity and gives the air in the bottle more room.

2. The air in the bottle expands and its pressure decreases.

3. The atmospheric pressure on the water surface in the tank forces water up into the low pressure space in the bottle and produces the fountain.

121—*f*. The water runs by gravity from the upper bottle into the lower bottle and it thereby does two things:

1. It decreases the air pressure in the upper bottle and permits the atmospheric pressure on the water in the milk bottle to produce the fountain in the upper bottle.

2. It increases the air pressure in the lower bottle and this increased pressure produces the lower fountain.

122—Similar to 120 and 121.

123—Directions.

124—The atmosphere at sea level can support a water column 34 feet high if there is a vacuum at the top of the column. In practice the height is only about 30 feet because air and water vapor escape from the water into the top space and exert pressure downward. For these reasons the maximum height of a water siphon is about 30 feet.

The upward pressure of the atmosphere at the bottom of the short arm of a siphon is a trifle less than the upward pressure of the atmosphere at the bottom of the long column because there is less air above it. In practice they are considered to be equal.

The liquid in a siphon always moves up in the short arm and down in the long arm, because the back pressure of the liquid in the short arm is always less than that in the long arm.

125—Similar to 124.

126—Similar to 120.

127—When you stop the flow from the tank, water continues to flow down the long rubber tube by gravity. This gives more space to the air in the large glass tube, coupling, and upper part of the balloon. This air expands and its pressure decreases. The atmospheric pressure on the outside of the balloon then forces the colored water out of the balloon into the large glass tube, whence it flows down the long rubber tube by gravity.

128—The water flowing by gravity from the upper bottle into the lower bottle does two things:

1. It gives more space to the air in the upper bottle and thereby permits its volume to increase and its pressure to decrease. The atmosphere then forces air into the upper bottle.

2. It drives the air out of the lower bottle.

129—*a.* The discharge siphon, like any other siphon, starts as soon as the water in the bottle has driven all the air out of the siphon. It continues to run until the water in the bottle falls below the lower end of the short arm.

b. The discharge siphon here consists of the bottle and vertical tube. To start this siphon, after the first discharge, the water in the bottle must rise above the top of the vertical pipe a distance equal to the depth of the U-tube. Because it must rise this distance to overcome the back pressure of the water in the U-tube when it drives the air out of the siphon.

130—A siphon stops flowing when it fills with air.

a. Here the arms of the siphon are small and the air moving into it at high velocity carries nearly all the water out of the trap.

b. Here the middle arm is so large that the rapidly moving air cannot remove all of the water it contains.

131—The water moving down the discharge tube produces at the top of the siphon a pressure less than that of the atmosphere and the atmosphere outside forces air into this low-pressure space through the vent pipe.

132—The flow is less through the nozzle because its outlet is smaller than that of the open tube.

133—The theoretical equation for the flow of liquids is: $v^2 = 2\ gh$
where : $v =$ velocity in feet per second;

$g = 32$, the acceleration in feet per sec. due to gravity;

$h =$ head in feet.

With a head of 1 foot:

$v^2 = 2 \times 32 \times 1 = 64$; $v = \sqrt{64} = 8$ feet per second.

With a head of 4 feet:

$v^2 = 2 \times 32 \times 4 = 256$; $v = \sqrt{256} = 16$ feet per second.

Air Compressed and Expanded

134—When you blow air into the bottle you increase the air pressure in the bottle and this increased pressure produces the fountain.

135—Similar to 134.

136—Important directions.

137—*Boyle's Law is:*

1. The volume of a given weight of gas varies inversely as the pressure on it.

2. The pressure of a confined gas is proportional to the amount of gas in the confining vessel.

3. The pressure exerted by a gas is always equal to the pressure on it.

Examples of Boyle's law:

The following table shows the results if we start with 1 gallon of gas under a pressure of 1 atmosphere and vary the pressure.

Atmospheres pressure	Volume in gallons
2	$\frac{1}{2}$
5	$\frac{1}{5}$
10	$\frac{1}{10}$
$\frac{1}{2}$	2
$\frac{1}{5}$	5
$\frac{1}{10}$	10

    a. The air in the open bottle was under a pressure of 1 atmosphere and its pressure was 1 atmosphere.
     When you fill the inverted bottle half full of water you compress the air to $\frac{1}{2}$ its first volume and its pressure is 2 atmospheres.

    b. The compressed air at 2 atmospheres pressure forces the water out against an outside pressure of 1 atmosphere. The moving pressure is then $2 - 1 = 1$ atmosphere, at the start.
     As the compressed air expands its pressure decreases and when it again fills the bottle its pressure will be 1 atmosphere.

138—Similar to 137.

139—The air pumped into the bottle increases the air pressure in the bottle and this air pressure produces the fountain.

140—The bottle acts as an air chamber. See 137 and 139.

141—The plunger moving into the large glass tube compresses the air in the tube and thereby increases its pressure.
    This increased pressure drives out the stopper.

142—Similar to 141.

143—*a*. The water saturates the air with water vapor.

  b. When you compress the air and water vapor you do work on them and this work turns into heat which radiates away rapidly.

  c. The air and water vapor do work in driving the plunger upward. This work is obtained from the heat contained in them and they cool. The water vapor on cooling condenses to millions of minute water drops which are *visible* as *mist*.

  d. When you compress the gases again you do work on them and this work turns into heat. The millions of visible water drops are turned into water vapor by this heat and become *invisible* again.

144—*Henry's Law is:* If a gas does not combine chemically with a liquid, the amount of gas dissolved in the liquid at a given temperature is directly proportional to the pressure on the gas and liquid.

  Example. A quart of water will dissolve about $\frac{3}{100}$ quarts of air at 32° F. and 1 atmosphere pressure.

  If the pressure is raised to 2 atmospheres the volume dissolved is doubled.

  If the pressure is decreased to $\frac{1}{100}$ atmosphere the volume dissolved is $\frac{1}{100}$ as much and $\frac{99}{100}$ of the dissolved gas leaves the liquid.

  d. When you raise the plunger you reduce the air pressure on the water almost to zero and most of the dissolved air bubbles out of the water at once.

  The escaping air bubbles are large because the pressure on them is very low, but the actual amount of air in them is small. This is shown by the small size of the air bubble left above the water when you let the plunger down and the pressure on the air becomes 1 atmosphere again.

145—*c*. The air in the tube expands and thereby decreases its pressure, when you give it more room.

  d. The atmosphere drives the plunger in against the low pressure exerted by the air in the tube.

146—*b*. The atmosphere lifts the water into the syringe.

  c. You drive the water out.

147—*c*. You force air from the syringe into the bottle and thereby increase the air pressure in the bottle.

  d. This increased air pressure lifts water into the syringe and raises the plunger.

148—When the water is stationary, its pressure downward is balanced by the upward pressure of the air. The water and the air each has potential energy due to its pressure. When you start the water moving you give it energy of motion or kinetic energy. The water in flowing downward compresses the air in the lower bottle and by the time it is brought to rest it has increased the pressure energy of the air by an amount equal to the kinetic energy of the water.

The air now has a pressure energy greater than the pressure energy of the water. It moves upward and gains kinetic energy but loses pressure energy. It stops when these two energies are balanced by the pressure energy of the water.

The pressure energy of the water is now greater than the pressure energy of the air. It starts moving downward and the operations are repeated until the bottomless bottle is empty.

149—See Newton's Third Law of Motion, Experience 95. The expanding air moves the water backward and the balloon forward with equal and opposite forces.

150—*a.* You set the air column vibrating so violently that it produces a musical note; and the shorter the air column the more rapid the vibration and the higher the pitch of the note.

    b. When you suck air out you decrease the air pressure in the tube and the atmosphere outside lifts the plunger.

       When you blow air in you increase the air pressure in the tube and this pressure drives the plunger down.

151—*b.* The steam drives nearly all the air out of the milk bottle.

    c. When the steam condenses to water it leaves nearly a complete vacuum in the milk bottle and the air in the second milk bottle expands the balloon into this vacuum.

152—Air is much lighter than water, volume for volume, hence the mixture of air bubbles and water in the large glass tube is much lighter than an equal depth of water outside the tube; and it is lifted over the edge of the pail by the upward force of this outside water.

OTHER GASES

153—Carbon-tetrachloride gas (CCl_4) neither burns nor supports combustion and it is 5.3 times as heavy as air. It settles down around the fire and smothers it by excluding air.

154—The fire is extinguished partly by the water and partly by the carbon-dioxide gas (CO_2) which neither burns nor supports combustion and is about 1.5 times as heavy as air.

See 49 for the chemical equation.

155—A level tablespoonful of baking soda when placed in dilute vinegar produces about 2 quarts of carbon-dioxide (CO_2) gas. This gas then exerts pressure on the water in the large bottle and produces the long stream.

156—The blue package of the Seidlitz powder contains Rochelle
salts, $C\,HOH\,COOK$ and cream of tartar $C\,HOH\,COOK$.

$\quad\quad\quad C\,HOH\,COONa \quad\quad\quad\quad\quad\quad C\,HOH\,COOH$

The white package contains baking soda, $Na\,H\,CO_3$.

Sometimes the baking soda is in the blue package and the cream of tartar in the white.

These salts, when mixed in water, produce about a pint of carbon-dioxide (CO_2) gas. The Rochelle salts take no part in the action, but the cream of tartar or acid-potassium tartrate, and baking soda react to produce more Rochelle salts, or sodium-potassium tartrate and carbon-dioxide gas.

The equation is:

$C\,HOH\,COOH \quad\quad\quad\quad\quad\quad C\,HOH\,COOK$

$C\,HOH\,COOK + Na\,H\,CO_3 \rightarrow C\,HOH\,COONa$

Cream of tartar + Baking soda → Rochelle salts
$\quad\quad\quad\quad\quad\quad + H_2O + CO_2$
$\quad\quad\quad\quad\quad\quad$ + Water + Carbon dioxide.

The pressure of the gas produces the fountain.

157—The zinc dissolves in the hydrochloric acid and produces hydrogen. The equation is:
$Zn + 2H\,Cl \quad\quad\quad \rightarrow Zn\,Cl_2 \quad\quad\quad + H_2$
Zinc + hydrochloric acid → zinc chloride + hydrogen.

158—The water pressure drives the hydrogen out of the bottle into the balloon.

The balloon rises to the ceiling because hydrogen weighs only about $\frac{1}{14}$ as much as air volume for volume. The buoyant force on the balloon is equal to the weight of the air it displaces. See also 43, 44, and the Law of Archimedes for gases, 45.

159—When hydrogen burns in air it combines with oxygen and produces water. The equation is
$$2H_2 \quad\quad + O_2 \quad\quad \rightarrow 2H_2O$$
Hydrogen + Oxygen → Water

The bubble filled with hydrogen rises to the ceiling for the reason given in 43, 44 and 45.

160—The kinetic theory of gases is: The molecules of all gases are in continuous rapid motion and the higher the temperature the more rapid the motion.

Each molecule moves only an extremely short distance before it collides with another molecule but it moves very rapidly between collisions.

The velocities of different kinds of molecules vary inversely as the square root of their molecular weights. That is, the lighter the molecule the greater its velocity. For example, the molecular weight of hydrogen (H_2) is 2, and that of oxygen (O_2) is 32. Their ratio is 32 to 2 or 16 to 1.

Then: $\dfrac{\text{velocity of hydrogen molecules}}{\text{velocity of oxygen molecules}} = \sqrt{\dfrac{16}{1}}$ or $\dfrac{4}{1}$

Hydrogen molecules move 4 times as fast as oxygen molecules. At 32° F. hydrogen molecules move with a velocity of about 6,000 feet a second and oxygen molecules 1,500 feet a second.

    d. e. The hydrogen molecules are much smaller and much faster than the oxygen and nitrogen molecules of the air. They move through the paper into the cylinder much faster than the air molecules can move out and they increase the gas pressure in the cylinder.

When you remove the hydrogen bottle, the hydrogen molecules move out through the paper more rapidly than the air molecules can move in, and they leave a temporary low pressure space in the cylinder. The atmosphere then lifts water up toward or into the cylinder.

Note. If you wish to keep hydrogen in the bottles over night, be sure to leave a half-inch or more of water over the cap of the inverted bottle. Hydrogen diffuses rapidly through cardboard but slowly through water.

161—The sodium perborate reacts with boiling water and produces oxygen, as follows:

$NaBO_3$ $+ H_2O$ $\rightarrow NaBO_2$
Sodium perborate + Water $\rightarrow$ Sodium metaborate
                               $+ H_2O_2$
                               + hydrogen peroxide.

         H_2O_2 $\rightarrow H_2O$ $+ O$
     Hydrogen peroxide $\rightarrow$ Water + Oxygen

b. Pure oxygen is five times as rich in oxygen as is air and supports combustion five times as readily.

Air is about ⅕ oxygen and ⅘ nitrogen.

162—At 70° F. the weight per 1,000 cubic feet is: for air about 75 lbs., for natural gas about 45 lbs., and for coal gas about 30 lbs. That is, fuel gases are, as a rule, lighter than air, volume for volume.

c. The bubble rises for the reason given in 43, 44 and 45.

163—Directions.

164—Directions

165—The balloon sinks when the water which clings to its surface makes its weight greater than that of the air it displaces.

BERNOULLI EFFECT

166—*The Bernoulli Effect is:* A rapidly moving stream of gas or liquid produces a low-pressure space around it, and the greater the velocity the lower is the pressure. See also Experiences 1 to 16.

d. The rapid stream of air produces low pressure in the nozzle, and the atmosphere pressing down on the water in the bottle lifts water to the top of the nozzle. Here the rapid stream of air breaks the water up into very small particles.

e. The ping-pong ball remains in the rapid air stream because as soon as it starts to fall out in any direction, there is low pressure on its inner side, Bernoulli Effect, and the atmospheric pressure on its outer side shoves it back into the air stream.

167—a. The ping-pong ball remains in the water stream for the reason given in 166—e.

b. The greatest difference in velocity and hence the lowest pressure is between the rapid water stream and the bottle at rest. The atmospheric pressure on the outer side of the water stream keeps it pressed against the bottle.

168—Each particle of water in the bottle has two velocities. One velocity is in a horizontal circle and it has a centrifugal effect which tends to keep the particle away from the center. The second velocity is downward toward the outlet.

Each particle moves once around its circular path in the same time that every other particle does, nearly. From this fact it follows that a particle near the center has a small circular velocity because its circle is small. Hence the centrifugal force on it is slight and its downward velocity has nearly its full effect. The downward velocity of particles near the center produces a pressure below that of the atmosphere, the Bernoulli Effect, and the atmosphere forces air into this low-pressure space. This explains why air is "sucked down" at the center.

LIQUIDS

169—Similar to No. 52.

170—Similar to No. 52.

171—The upward pressure at any depth under a liquid is equal to the downward pressure at that depth.

The upward pressure on the under side of the paper is equal to the downward pressure of a column of liquid measured from the paper to the surface of the liquid.

172—*b*. The upward force of the water compresses the air in the bottle and the compressed air expands the balloon.

c. The upward pressure of the water at the mouth of the bottle produces the fountain.

173—The buoyant force of the water is equal to the weight of the water displaced. When you blow air in you increase the amount of water displaced and thereby increase the buoyant force of the water.

When you suck air out you decrease the amount of water displaced and thereby decrease the buoyant force of the water.

174—The full bottle weighs more at first than the weight of the water it displaces, hence it sinks to the bottom of the pail.

The bottle rises above the bottom as soon as its total weight is reduced to equal the weight of water it displaces. Once it is above the bottom it floats at such a depth that the weight of the displaced water is exactly equal to its total weight.

175—*a*. Kerosene weighs $\frac{8}{10}$ as much as water, volume for volume, hence a kerosene column is always $\frac{10}{8}$ the height of the water column it balances.

b. The atmospheric pressure on the water in the tumbler is equal to that on the kerosene, also the air pressures above the liquid columns are equal. The kerosene column is $\frac{10}{8}$ the height of the water column for the reason given in *a*.

176—*Newton's Third Law of Motion is:* To every action there is an equal and opposite reaction.

The water stream exerts equal and opposite forces on the water in the pail and on the elbow, and it drives them in opposite directions.

177—e. The phenomenon of osmosis is: When a strong solution is separated from a weak solution by a membrane which the liquid can penetrate but the dissolved substance cannot penetrate, the liquid always moves from the weak solution into the strong solution.

In this case water is a very weak solution and it passes through the cellophane into the strong salt solution. This osmosis causes the strong salt solution to rise in the coupling.

178—Similar to 177.

179—The water moves through each cell wall into the strong blood solution in the cell with such great osmotic force that it bursts the cell and lets the blood out.

180—The soap film on the small bubble has exactly the same contracting force or surface tension as the film on the large bubble, but it acts on a smaller amount of air and produces a greater internal air pressure which forces its air over into the larger bubble.

HEAT

181—The dry ice is at a temperature of about minus 110° F., and if the tap water is at say 60° F., the difference in temperature is 170° F. The dry ice turns to gas rapidly and expands the balloon and produces the water streams. See also 68 and 69.

182—The steam issues from the nozzle at high velocity and drives the turbine.

183—The steam drives the air out of the bottle and leaves nearly a complete vacuum when it condenses to water. The atmosphere outside lifts water into this low-pressure space in the bottle and produces the fountain.

184—a. The steam lifts the stopper, then some steam escapes, and the steam pressure decreases enough to let the stopper drop down. The steam pressure increases again and lifts the stopper, and the operations are repeated.

b. Similar to a.

185—The gas burns rapidly and produces a great deal of heat which expands the gases rapidly. This rapid gas expansion is the "explosion" which lifts the can.

186—b. Air is heavier volume for volume than the fuel gas. It enters the lower hole and lifts the lighter fuel gas upward and out through the upper hole. Here the gas burns in air which enters the flame from the sides.

c. By the time the flame is low, the remaining gas and the air in the can have mixed somewhat by diffusion, and when the flame ducks down into the hole, the mixture of gas and air burns very rapidly, and produces heat very rapidly which expands the gases in the can very rapidly. That is, the mixture "explodes."

187—Similar to 185.

188—The fine lycopodium powder burns very rapidly in the air in the can when it is lighted by the candle. It produces an explosion for the reasons given in 185 and 186.

189—These are three ways of showing that air expands when it is heated.

190—These experiences show that air expands when heated and contracts when cooled.

191—The siphon draws water out of the bottle and leaves more space for the air in the bottle. The air then expands and its pressure decreases. The atmosphere outside then pushes smoke through the burning smoke producer into the bottle.

192—The cool air outside the bottle is heavier, volume for volume, than the hot air in the bottle. It sinks down around the bottle, enters the bottle at the bottom, and lifts the lighter hot air out through the neck.

The smoke shows the motion of this convection current in air.

193—Each tap on the rubber compresses the smoke quickly and forces a smoke ring out of the mouth of the tank.

194—Water expands when heated and contracts when cooled.

195—Cold water is heavier, volume for volume, than hot water. The cold water in the upper bottle sinks into the lower bottle and lifts the lighter hot colored water up into the upper bottle. This movement is called a convection current.

196—The air in the bottle expands when you suck air out. It does work in this expansion and this work is obtained from its own heat. It cools and the water vapor it contains condenses into millions of small *visible* water particles or *mist*.

When you let air into the bottle, the atmosphere outside forces the air in and it does work on the air in the bottle in compressing it again. This work turns into heat which warms the air and water particles enough to make the water particles evaporate into *invisible* water vapor. See also 143.

197—When salt water is boiled the salt remains in the boiler but the water turns to steam and the steam, when cooled, condenses to water free from salt.

198—Water open to the air dissolves a certain amount of air and the cooler the water the greater is the amount dissolved. When the water is heated to the boiling point most of this dissolved air is given up. See also 144.

199—Method.

200—a. The ether evaporates very rapidly and takes its heat of evaporation from itself and its surroundings. It does this so rapidly that its temperature falls below the freezing point of water. It takes heat from the water under the cap and freezes it.

b. Similar to a.

c. The ether evaporates very rapidly when it is warmed by the hot water. It produces a large amount of ether vapor which exerts pressure on the water and produces the fountain.

INDEX